AQA KS3

Science 1

Know and apply

PRACTICE BOOK

Cliff Curtis
Deborah Lowe
Owen Mansfield

HODDER
EDUCATION
AN HACHETTE UK COMPANY

Hachette UK's policy is to use papers that are natural, renewable and recyclable products and made from wood grown in sustainable forests. The logging and manufacturing processes are expected to conform to the environmental regulations of the country of origin.

Orders: please contact Bookpoint Ltd, 130 Park Drive, Milton Park, Abingdon, Oxon OX14 4SE. Telephone: (44) 01235 827720. Fax: (44) 01235 400454. Email education@bookpoint.co.uk Lines are open from 9 a.m. to 5 p.m., Monday to Saturday, with a 24-hour message answering service. You can also order through our website: www.hoddereducation.co.uk

First published in 2017 by
Hodder Education,
An Hachette UK Company
Carmelite House
50 Victoria Embankment
London EC4Y 0DZ

www.hoddereducation.co.uk

Impression number 10 9 8 7 6 5 4 3 2

Year 2021 2020 2019 2018

Cover photo © PCN Photography / Alamy Stock Photo

Typeset in 12/14 pt Vectora 45 Light by Integra Software Services Pvt. Ltd., Pondicherry, India

Printed in India

A catalogue record for this title is available from the British Library.

ISBN: 9781471899973

Contents

Find the answers at www.hoddereducation.co.uk/AQAKS3Science

1 Speed

» Calculating speed

Worked example

A sprinter runs 400 m in 50 seconds.

a) What is her average speed?
b) How far would she run in 1.5 minutes at this speed?
c) How long would it take her to run 1 km at this speed?

a) Using the average speed equation:

$$\text{average speed} = \frac{\text{distance travelled}}{\text{time taken}} = \frac{400\,\text{m}}{50\,\text{s}} = 8\,\text{m/s}$$

b) Rearranging the equation and remembering that time should be in seconds:

$$\text{distance travelled} = \text{average speed} \times \text{time taken} = (8\,\text{m/s}) \times 90\,\text{s} = 720\,\text{m}$$

c) Rearranging the equation and remembering that 1 km is 1000 m:

$$\text{time taken} = \frac{\text{distance travelled}}{\text{average speed}} = \frac{1000\,\text{m}}{8\,\text{m/s}} = 125\,\text{s}$$

> **Hint**
>
> If you want to find the distance travelled or the time taken, you have to rearrange the equation.

Know

1 What does speed tell us about an object?

2 What do we need to know to calculate the average speed of an object?

3 Person A takes longer than person B to walk the same distance. Who has the higher speed?

4 An object is travelling at a steady speed. What will happen to an object's speed when the following forces are applied to them?

In (A) no forces are acting on the object. In (B) an unbalanced force is acting on the object in the same direction that it is travelling. In (C) balanced forces are acting on the object. In (D) an unbalanced force is acting on the object in the opposite direction from the way in which it is travelling.

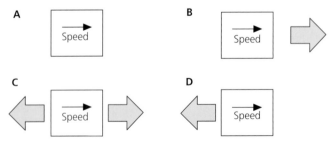

5 What is the equation for average speed?

6 How would you rearrange this equation for:

   a) distance travelled

   b) time taken?

7 State some different units that speed can be measured in.

8 What would be the most sensible unit of speed to use for a question that gives:

   a) distance in metres and time in minutes

   b) time in hours and distance in miles

   c) distance in kilometres and speed in seconds?

9 What is the average speed of a dog that travels 60 m in 5 s?

10 What is the average speed of a bicycle that travels 50 km in 2 h?

11 What is the average speed of a rocket that travels 100 km in 25 s?

12 Copy and complete the table below. The first two have been done for you.

Speed	Distance	Time
5 m/s	100 m	20 s
8 km/h	4 km	30 min
	48 m	4 s
	125 m	25 s
2 m/s	8 m	
24 m/s		10 s
40 km/h		3 h
	20 km	5 h
15 km/s	90 km	
3 m/s		1 h

Apply

1 A boy walks 200 m in 40 seconds.

   a) What is his average speed?

   b) How far would he walk in 5 minutes at this speed?

   c) How many minutes would it take him to walk 2.5 km at this speed?

2 The speed limit on busy roads in the UK is 30 miles per hour.

   a) How long would it take a car travelling at this speed on average to travel 90 miles?

   b) How long would it take a car travelling at this speed on average to travel 10 miles?

   c) How far would a car travelling at this speed on average travel in 45 minutes?

» Finding speed from a graph

Worked example

The distance–time graph below shows Izzie's journey to the corner shop.

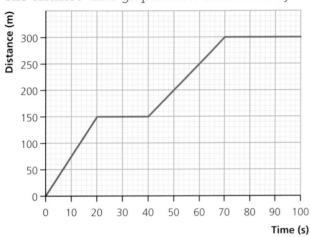

a) Between what times is she:
   i)   travelling at a steady speed
   ii) stationary
   iii) travelling the fastest?
b) How far does Izzie travel in total?
c) What is Izzie's speed between 40 s and 70 s?
d) What is Izzie's average speed for the whole journey?

> **Hint**
>
> Gradient is calculated by dividing the change in *y* value (up) by the change in *x* value (across).

a) From the graph we can see that:
   i)   Izzie is travelling at a steady speed from 0–20 s and from 40–70 s, because these parts of the graph are straight diagonal lines.
   ii) Izzie is stationary from 20–40 seconds and from 70–100 seconds, because these are the horizontal parts of the graph.
   iii) Izzie is travelling the fastest from 0–20 s, because this is the steepest part of the graph.
b) 300 m – this is the highest value reached by the graph on the *y*-axis, which shows distance.
c) The speed is calculated using the gradient:
$$\text{gradient} = \frac{\text{change in } y \text{ value}}{\text{change in } x \text{ value}} = \frac{300 - 150}{70 - 40} = \frac{150}{30} = 5 \text{ m/s}$$
d) This is calculated using the total distance and the total time taken:
$$\text{average speed} = \frac{\text{distance travelled}}{\text{time taken}} = \frac{300 \text{ m}}{100 \text{ s}} = 3 \text{ m/s}$$

Know

1 Copy and complete the following paragraph:

On a distance–time graph, an object moving at a steady speed is represented by a _____ straight line. The _____ the line, the faster the object is moving, because the speed is equal to the _____ (or slope) of the line. When an object is _____, the graph will show a horizontal line. When it is accelerating (_____ up or _____ down), the graph will be a _____.

2 Look at the four distance–time graphs below.

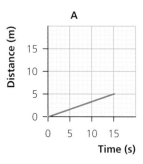

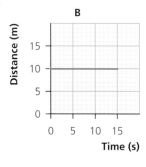

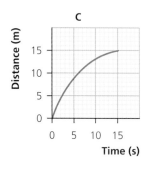

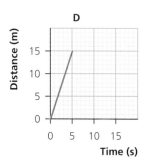

a) Label each of the graphs with one of the following captions: fast steady speed, slow steady speed, accelerating, stationary.

b) For the two steady-speed graphs, calculate the speeds that are represented.

Apply

1 Look at the graph of an elephant's journey below.

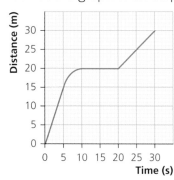

a) When is the elephant travelling at a steady speed?

b) When is the elephant stationary?

c) When is the elephant accelerating?

d) How far does the elephant travel in total?

e) What is the elephant's speed between 0 s and 5 s?

f) What is the elephant's speed between 20 s and 30 s?

g) What is the elephant's average speed for the whole journey?

2 Draw a distance–time graph for the following journey. Your *x*-axis scale should go up to 10 seconds and your *y*-axis scale should go up to 10 metres.

- The object travels 6 m in the first 3 s.

- It is then stationary for 2 s.

- It then travels 4 m in the next 5 s.

Use the graph to calculate the speed of the object during each part of its journey, and then the average speed for the whole journey.

» Relative speed

Worked example

A train is travelling at 50 km/h. A car on a road running parallel next to the track is travelling at 30 km/h. Calculate the relative speed of the train and car when:

a) the car and train are travelling in the same direction
b) the car and train are travelling in opposite directions.

a) *When two objects are travelling in the same direction, the relative speed between them is the difference between their speeds:*

relative speed = fastest speed – slowest speed

relative speed = 50 km/h – 30 km/h = 20 km/h

b) *When two objects are travelling in opposite directions, the relative speed between them is the sum of their speeds:*

relative speed = fastest speed + slowest speed

relative speed = 50 km/h + 30 km/h = 80 km/h

Know

1 Copy and complete the paragraph below:

The relative speed of objects depends on their _____ motion. If two objects are moving in the same direction, you must find the _____ between the two speeds to find the relative _____ of the objects. However, if they are travelling in _____ directions, the relative speed is the sum of the two speeds; you need to _____ them up.

2 Car A is travelling at 30 km/h, whilst car B is travelling at 40 km/h. What is the relative speed between them if they are:

a) both travelling in the same direction

b) travelling in opposite directions?

Apply

1 Lifts 1 and 2 both travel at 10 m/s. What is their relative speed when:

    a) they are both going up

    b) lift 1 is going up and lift 2 is going down

    c) they are both going down

    d) lift 1 is stationary and lift 2 is going up?

» Acceleration

Worked example

A Formula 1 racing car accelerates from stationary to 120 m/s in 4 s. A normal car reaches the same speed in 8 s. Which has a greater acceleration?

Acceleration tells us how quickly an object can speed up or slow down. Therefore, an object that reaches a speed in a shorter time than another has a higher rate of acceleration. As the Formula 1 car can reach 120 m/s in half the speed of the normal car, it must have the greater acceleration.

Know

1 What is acceleration?

2 Which of the following cars would be accelerating?

    a) A car braking at traffic lights.

    b) A car waiting for the traffic lights to change.

    c) A car starting to move when the green light of the traffic lights comes on.

    d) A car travelling steadily at 70 mph on the motorway.

3 Put these accelerations in order, from the smallest acceleration to the largest:

    A An aeroplane taking off.

    B A sprinter starting to run the 100 m.

    C A car starting as the traffic lights turn green.

    D A jogger starting to run a marathon.

    E A child starting to walk to school.

    F A baby starting to crawl across the room.

Apply

1 How do we represent acceleration on a distance–time graph?

2 Sketch a distance–time graph for objects A and B, where object B is speeding up more quickly than object A.

2 Gravity

» Mass and weight

Worked example

The suits worn by Neil Armstrong and other astronauts on the Apollo missions to the Moon had a mass of approximately 90 kg.

a) What was the weight of these suits at the Earth's surface?
b) On the Moon, the suits only weighed 144 N, because there is less gravity there. Calculate the gravitational field strength on the surface of the Moon.
c) Why is gravitational field strength weaker on the Moon?

a) Using the equation:

weight = mass × gravitational field strength
weight = 90 kg × 10 N/kg = 900 N

b) Here, we need to rearrange the equation so that:

$$\text{gravitational field strength} = \frac{\text{weight}}{\text{mass}} = \frac{144}{90} = 1.6 \, \text{N/kg}$$

c) The gravitational field strength of a planet or moon depends on its mass. The Moon is much smaller than the Earth, and so has less mass. Therefore, its gravitational field strength is smaller too.

> **Hint**
>
> g has a value of 10 N/kg at the Earth's surface.

Know

1 What force causes mass to have weight?

2 What is mass measured in?

3 What is weight measured in?

4 What equation links mass and weight?

5 What symbol does gravitational field strength have?

6 What is the value of gravitational field strength on Earth?

7 What two factors does the value of g depend on?

8 What would the weight of a book that had a mass of 1 kg be?

9 What is the mass and weight of the apple in the picture?

10 Person A has twice the mass of person B. Who would weigh more? By how much?

Apply

1 'I weigh 60 kg.' What is wrong with this statement? How could it be corrected?

2 Put these objects in order of the gravitational field strength they would have at their surface and then explain your thinking: Sun, Moon, Earth, Jupiter.

3 What is the weight of an 8 kg dog?

4 What is the mass of a bag of potatoes that has a weight of 50 N?

5 How would the gravitational field strength of Earth change if the Earth was:

   a) more massive

   b) less massive?

6 A 2 kg mass weighs 46.2 N on Jupiter. What is the value of *g* on Jupiter?

7 Copy and complete the table below:

Mass	Weight (on Earth)
2 kg	
48.6 kg	
	150 N
	6.8 N
100 g	
38 g	
	0.9 N

Hint

When working out the weight of an object, the mass must be in kilograms.

3 Voltage and resistance

» Voltage

Worked example

The circuit below contains three 3V cells and two identical bulbs.

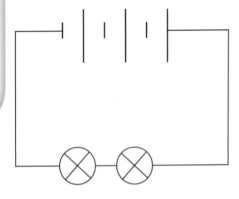

a) What is the total potential difference provided by the cells?

b) What would the potential difference across each bulb be?

c) One of the bulbs is taken away. What would the potential difference across the remaining bulb be now?

d) One of the cells is taken away. What would the potential difference across the single bulb be in this situation?

a) The three cells are all connected in the same direction, so the potential difference across them is simply 3 × 3v = 9v.

b) The bulbs are identical and the circuit is connected in series. This means that the potential difference provided by the cells must be shared equally between the two bulbs. Therefore, each bulb will have 9v ÷ 2 = 4.5v of potential difference across it.

c) The total potential difference across all components in a series circuit must equal the potential difference across the power supply. As there is now only one component – the single bulb – the potential difference across this must be 9v.

d) Taking a cell away reduces the potential difference of the power supply to 2 × 3v = 6v. Therefore, the potential difference across the single bulb must be 6v too, as the bulb cannot have a higher voltage than the power supply.

> **Hint**
>
> A component is a device in a circuit that uses electrical energy and transfers it to some other form. For example, a light bulb transfers electrical energy to light (and heat) energy.

Know

1 Draw the circuit symbols for:

   a) a cell

   b) a bulb

   c) a wire.

2 Write a definition for potential difference.

3 What piece of equipment is used to measure potential difference? Draw the circuit symbol for this.

4 What is the job of a power supply (such as a cell) in an electric circuit?

5 What is the difference between a cell and a battery?

6 Which of the following electric circuits will not work? Why?

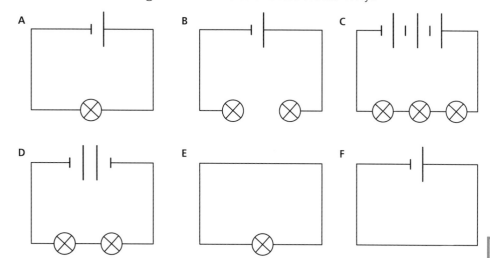

Apply

1 Each of the cells in the diagrams below has a potential difference of 1.5 V. Calculate the potential difference of each battery of cells.

   a)   b)   c)

> **Hint**
>
> If a cell is connected in the opposite direction from the other cell, its potential difference must be taken away to find the total potential difference across the battery.

2 The bulbs and cells in the diagram below are all identical. How would the brightness of the bulbs in circuits B, C and D compare with the bulb in circuit A? Explain why.

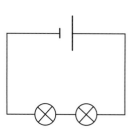   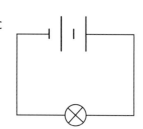   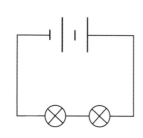

» Resistance

Worked example

The circuit contains a cell and two resistors (A and B) in series. The current at all points is 2 A.

a) What must the potential difference across resistor B be?
b) Calculate the resistance of the two resistors individually.
c) What is the total resistance of the circuit?

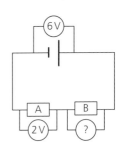

a) The potential difference across the cell is shared between components in a series circuit. Therefore the potential difference across resistor B must be 6 V − 2 V = 4 V.

b) For this, we need to use the equation:

$$resistance = \frac{voltage}{current}$$

For resistor A:

$$resistance = \frac{voltage}{current} = \frac{2\,V}{2\,A} = 1\,\Omega$$

For resistor B:

$$resistance = \frac{voltage}{current} = \frac{4\,V}{2\,A} = 2\,\Omega$$

c) Resistors in series add up. Therefore, the total resistance = 1 Ω + 2 Ω = 3 Ω.

Know

1 What is the difference between a conductor and an insulator?

2 Group the following into conductors and insulators: copper, wood, plastic, nickel, iron, paper, aluminium.

3 What does the resistance of a material tell us?

4 Write a definition for current.

5 What piece of equipment is current measured with?

6 What equation links resistance, voltage and current?

7 Copy and complete the table on the right. The first row has been done for you.

Resistance (Ω)	Voltage (V)	Current (A)
2	10	5
	9	3
	15	2
8	24	
3	12	
2		7
10		8

Apply

1 A resistor has a potential difference across it of 5 V and current passing through it of 2 A. Calculate its resistance.

2 What would the potential difference across a 10 Ω resistor be when a current of 3 A passes through it?

Hint

If you are trying to find potential difference or current in a problem, you will need to rearrange the equation.

4 Current

» Multiple loops

Worked example

The two circuits below both contain a 3V cell and two resistors. Circuit 1 is connected in series and circuit 2 is connected in parallel.

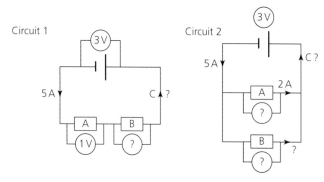

For circuit 1:

a) What would the potential difference across resistor B be?
b) What would the current at point C be?

For circuit 2:

c) What would the potential difference across resistors A and B be?
d) What would the current through resistor B and at point C be?

For circuit 1:

a) In a series circuit, the potential difference across all of the components in total must equal the potential difference across the power supply. Therefore, the potential difference across B must equal 3V − 1V = 2V.

b) In a series circuit, the current is the same everywhere. Therefore, the current at point C must also be 5A.

For circuit 2:

c) In a parallel circuit, the potential difference across each branch is equal to the potential difference across the power supply. Therefore, the potential difference across resistors A and B must each be 3V.

d) In a parallel circuit, the current through the branches must add up to the current passing through the power supply. Therefore, the current through resistor B must be 5A − 2A = 3A. The current at point C must be 5A, as this is when the branches have joined back together again.

> **Hint**
>
> The potential difference across or the current running through a resistor is not fixed – it can change depending on the arrangement of the circuit that it is in.

Know

1 Name the following circuit symbols:

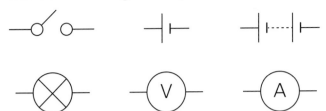

2 What does current tell us about a circuit?

3 State two ways in which you can increase the current in a circuit.

4 Put these components in order, from the best conductor to the best insulator.

Component	Resistance (Ω)
A	25
B	1000
C	2
D	500
E	30000
F	150

5 Which of the following are series circuits and which are parallel?

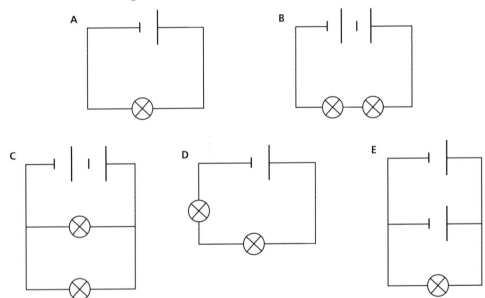

6 Delete the incorrect words in the sentences below.

a) The current in a series circuit is *the same/shared* everywhere but the potential difference is *the same/shared* across each component.

b) The current in a parallel circuit is *the same/shared* between branches but the potential difference is *the same/shared* across each branch.

7 What safety issues can a high current in a wire cause?

Apply

1 A bulb is connected to a battery. What will happen to the brightness of this bulb if an identical bulb is connected:

   a) in series

   b) in parallel?

   Explain why.

2 Look at the circuit below. Three identical bulbs are connected with a power supply in parallel.

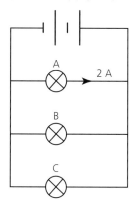

   a) If the current running through bulb A is 2A, what current must be passing through bulbs B and C?

   b) What would the current passing through the battery be?

   c) If the resistance of each bulb is 5Ω, what must the potential difference across each bulb be?

   d) Therefore, what must the potential difference across the battery be?

   e) Therefore, what must the potential difference across each of the two identical cells be individually?

» Statics

Worked example

When Aalia combs her hair, her comb becomes negatively charged.

a) Describe how this happens.
b) What would happen if she placed her comb near her hair? Why?
c) What would happen if she placed her comb near another negatively charged object? Why?

a) As Aalia combs her hair, negative electrons are transferred from her hair to the comb. This causes the comb to become negatively charged, and for her hair to become positively charged.
b) The comb and her hair would be attracted to each other, because they have the opposite charge; one is negative and one is positive.
c) The comb and the object would repel each other, because they have the same charge; they are both negative.

Know

1 What is an electron?

2 What would the charge on an object be if it had:

   a) gained electrons

   b) lost electrons?

3 Is the electrostatic force a contact or non-contact force? How do you know?

4 Complete the sentence: Like charges _____, opposite charges _____.

5 Will the following charges repel or attract?

   a)

   b)

   c)

   d)

   e)

   f)

Apply

1 What is created if positive and negative charges are separated?

2 What must the missing charges be in the following pairs?

   a)   b)   c)   d)

3 Put the following in order, from the biggest force of repulsion to the biggest force of attraction.

   A   B

   C   D   E

4 Static charge can be created by rubbing a balloon on a jumper or on your hair.

   a) Describe how the balloon becomes charged.

   b) A negative balloon sticks to the wall. What charge must the wall have? Why?

5 When you touch a Van de Graff generator, you become statically charged – electrons are transferred to or away from you. This can cause your hair to stand up on end. In what way must the electrons be transferred if you become:

   a) negatively charged

   b) positively charged?

5 Energy costs

» Energy

Worked example

A cyclist transfers about 800 kJ of energy every hour.

a) How many kJ of energy will a cyclist transfer in half an hour?
b) 100 g of chocolate contains about 2000 kJ. How long would it take a cyclist to transfer this much energy?

a) If the cyclist transfers 800 kJ in 1 hour, they will transfer
   800 × 0.5 = 400 kJ in half an hour.
b) For this, we need to divide the energy in 100 g of chocolate by the
   energy a cyclist transfers per hour. The time would equal
   2000 kJ ÷ 800 kJ = 2.5 hours.

Know

1 How many joules are in a kilojoule of energy?

2 Put these activities in order of how much energy they would transfer, from least to most.

   A watching TV

   B running 20 m for the bus

   C playing football for an hour

   D walking 1 mile to school

   E running a marathon

3 One banana contains about 400 kJ of energy. How much energy would there be in:

   a) a pair of bananas

   b) a bunch of seven bananas?

Apply

1 Different types of exercise 'burn off' different amounts of energy. The table on page 18 shows how much energy various activities transfer each half an hour.

Activity	Energy transferred per half an hour (kJ)
Aerobics	550
Basketball	700
Bowling	250
Dancing	450
Jogging	800
Stair climbing	650
Swimming	500
Walking	350

a) Which activity transfers the most energy per half an hour?

b) How much energy would you transfer if you:

    i) played basketball for 1 hour

    ii) bowled for 2 hours

    iii) jogged for 15 minutes

    iv) walked for 4 hours?

» Energy resources

Worked example

a) What are the main sources of energy in the UK? Are these renewable or not?

b) Would the following renewable energy sources be a good choice for the UK to invest in? Why?
i) wind power
ii) solar power
iii) tidal power

a) The main sources of energy in the UK are gas, coal and nuclear power. These are all non-renewable; the fuel supplies will eventually run out.

b) i) Wind power is a good choice for the UK, as it is quite a windy country. This means that wind turbines will be able to run most of the time.

ii) Solar power is not a good choice for the UK as it is not always sunny. Therefore solar panels would not be able to work a lot of the time.

iii) Tidal power is a good choice for the UK because it is an island, meaning that it has lots of coastlines where tidal power could be installed.

Know

1 What is an energy resource?

2 What is a fuel?

3 State the three main fossil fuels.

4 What is the difference between a non-renewable energy resource and a renewable one?

5 Sort the following energy resources into 'renewable' and 'non-renewable', and then give an advantage and a disadvantage for each.

    a) coal

    b) solar

    c) wind

    d) nuclear fuel

    e) oil

    f) biomass

    g) waves

    h) gas

    i) geothermal

Apply

1 Make a flow chart describing how fossil fuels were formed.

2 The world currently makes most of its energy using non-renewable energy sources. Suggest reasons why we are starting to use more renewable energy sources to make electricity.

3 Two countries (A and B) use the following proportions of energy resources:

Energy source	Percentage used by country	
	A	B
Coal	40%	30%
Oil	10%	30%
Gas	20%	20%
Nuclear	5%	0%
Wind	10%	1%
Solar	2%	15%
Tidal	8%	2%
Geothermal	5%	2%

    a) Which country uses the higher percentage of fossil fuels? How much more?

    b) Which country uses the higher percentage of renewable energy? How much more?

    c) Which country is more likely to be nearer the Equator? Why?

    d) Which country is more likely to be an island? Why?

    e) In total, country A transfers 200 MJ of energy each day, whilst country B transfers 500 MJ. Work out how many MJ must be produced by coal and wind in each country.

» Energy in the home

Worked example

A kettle is labelled 3 kW and is used for 2 hours each week. If electricity costs 11 p per kWh, how much does the kettle cost to operate?

To answer this question, we need to use the equation:

cost = power (kW) × time (hours) × price per kWh

It is important to have time in hours and power in kW when using this equation. Here, this is already done for us so we don't need to make any conversions – we can put the numbers straight into the equation:

cost = power (kW) × time (hours) × price per kWh

cost = 3 kW × 2 h × 11 p = 66 p

Know

1 What is power?

2 How many watts are in a kilowatt?

3 What equation can we use to calculate the cost of electricity? What units must each part be in?

Apply

1 Copy and complete the table below. The first row has been done for you.

Cost (p)	Power (kW)	Time (h)	Cost per kWh (p)
110	5	2	11
	3	6	11
	2	4	14
	1.5	7	14
80	8	1	
100		5	10
40	2		5

2 Here are some typical power ratings for everyday appliances. Copy the table and fill in the gaps.

Appliance	Power in W	Power in kW
Light bulb	100	0.1
Desktop computer	300	
Kettle		2
Fridge		0.2
Hairdryer	1500	
Electric shower		8
Washing machine	500	

6 Energy transfers

» Energy stores

Worked example

A pop up toy is pressed down and then released. Draw simple energy transfer diagrams for this situation.

When the toy is pressed down, it has filled its elastic store of energy. When it is released, this energy is transferred to its gravitational store, as it rises up in the air.

If we want to go one step further, we can think of the next energy transfer. Once the toy has reached the peak of its journey, it will fall back down again, transferring energy to its kinetic store as it speeds up.

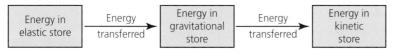

Know

1 What is the unit of energy?

2 When are the following energy stores filled?

   a) gravitational

   b) kinetic

   c) elastic

3 Simon pulls back an elastic band so that it stretches.

   a) What energy store is filled?

   b) He lets the elastic band go and it flies across the room. What energy store is filled now?

4 Raveena picks up a book from the floor.

   a) What energy store is filled?

   b) She drops the book again. What energy store is filled now?

Apply

1 Draw simple energy transfer diagrams for the following situations:

   a) Dropping an apple from a height.

   b) Heating up soup in a pan on a gas hob.

   c) Throwing a ball into the air.

   d) Jumping on a trampoline.

   e) Powering a motor with a battery.

» Energy dissipation

Worked example

A battery provides 400 J of energy for an electric buzzer. However, the buzzer only transfers 250 J of this energy.

a) What has happened to the energy that has gone 'missing'?

b) Which energy store has it been transferred to?

c) How much has been transferred in this way?

a) The 'missing' energy has not disappeared – it has been dissipated as heat. This means that it has been spread out and shared between more energy stores.

b) The energy has been transferred to the thermal stores of the surroundings – e.g. the wires of the circuit, the buzzer itself and the air around it.

c) Energy cannot be created or destroyed, so the energy dissipated must be equal to the difference between the energy provided by the battery and the energy used by the buzzer. Therefore, 400 J − 250 J = 150 J has been dissipated.

Know

1 What is the conservation of energy?

2 Why does energy dissipation reduce the amount of useful energy available?

3 How can you reduce the energy dissipated (or wasted) in:

   a) the moving parts of a car engine

   b) a house?

4 State three types of energy pathway.

5 What types of energy pathway are used to transfer energy when:

   a) a light bulb is switched on

   b) a radio is played

   c) a mobile phone charger is plugged in?

Apply

1 Copy and complete the table below. The first row has been done for you.

Energy put into system (J)	Energy usefully transferred in the system (J)	Energy dissipated in the system (J)	Percentage of energy used usefully
50	30	20	60%
100	80		
16	4		
500		250	
75		50	
	8	2	
200			90%
20			30%
40		8	
	17	3	
	30		50%

7 Sound

» Describing sound

Worked example

These are two oscilloscope traces showing two different sounds.

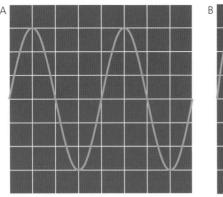
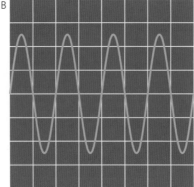

Assuming that each square counts for 1 cm vertically and 1 second horizontally:

a) determine the amplitude of each wave
b) determine the period of each wave
c) explain how the two sounds producing these waves would be different.

a) Amplitude is measured from the middle to the top of each wave. If each square represents 1 cm then wave A would have an amplitude of 3 cm and wave B would have an amplitude of 2.5 cm.

b) Period is measured horizontally between two identical points on two neighbouring waves (e.g. from peak to peak). If each square represents 1 second, then wave A would have a period of 4 seconds and wave B would have a period of 2 seconds.

c) Wave A would be produced by a louder sound than wave B because it has a larger amplitude. Wave B would be produced by a higher-pitched sound than wave A because it has a higher frequency; the waves are more 'bunched up'. So wave A would be lower but louder and wave B would be higher but quieter.

Know

1 Sounds are made up of vibrations; what is a vibration?

2 What is volume measured in?

3 Give an example of a sound that has:

   a) a high pitch

   b) a low pitch.

4 Identify the medium, source and detector in the diagram below.

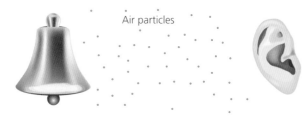

Air particles

5 What is the speed of sound in air?

6 Put these in order of how fast sound can travel through them, from slowest to fastest: solid, liquid, gas.

7 Define the following keywords, then label a) and b) on a copy of the diagram:

a) amplitude

b) period

c) frequency.

8 What piece of scientific equipment can be used to make a sound graph?

9 Look at the four wave diagrams below.

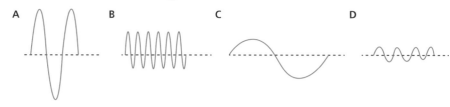

Which wave:

a) has the highest frequency

b) has the lowest frequency

c) has the largest amplitude

d) has the smallest amplitude

e) has the longest period

f) has the shortest period

g) is the quietest

h) is the loudest

i) has the highest pitch

j) has the lowest pitch?

10 Measure the amplitudes and periods of the two sound waves below. Which would be the loudest? Why?

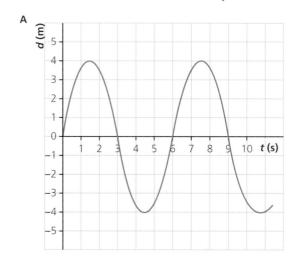

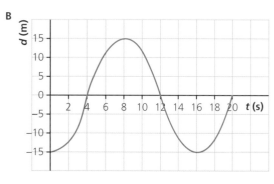

Apply

1 Sound is a longitudinal wave. What does this mean?

2 Why can't sound travel through a vacuum?

3 A bell rings. Describe how the sound travels from the bell to your ear.

4 What's wrong with the following wave diagrams?

a)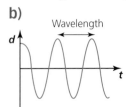

b)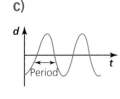

c)

5 200 waves pass a point in 5 seconds. What is the frequency of the waves?

» Ranges

Worked example

In recent years, 'mosquito' devices have been installed in areas where young people might loiter. They emit a sound that is about 18 kHz.

a) What is 18 kHz in Hz?

b) Explain why these devices will affect young people and older people differently?

a) Kilo (or k) means '1000', so 18 kHz is 18 000 Hz.

b) The human auditory (or hearing) range is 20 Hz to 20 000 Hz. 18 000 Hz is near the top of this range, so mosquito devices emit a very high-pitched sound. However, auditory range decreases with age; as humans get older, they cannot hear the highest sounds as well. Therefore, although younger people can hear this high-pitched sound, older people cannot, as their hearing range is now below 18 000 Hz.

Know

1 What does 'average auditory range' mean?

2 What is the average hearing range for humans?

3 Who is more likely to have a larger hearing range – an old man or a young girl? Why?

4 What is ultrasound?

5 How many hertz are in 1 kHz?

6 What is an echo? Give two examples of echoes in everyday life.

Apply

1 State some uses of ultrasound.

2 Look at the diagram of the ear.

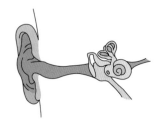

   a) Label a copy of the diagram using the keywords ear canal, eardrum, bones and cochlea.

   b) Give a simple description of the function of each of these parts.

3 Give some examples of how hearing can be damaged.

8 Light

» Transmitted light

Worked example

A bulb emits light that travels through a window to a person's eye. Use the keywords *absorb, transmit, reflect* and *refract* to describe the light ray's journey.

The ray of light is transmitted through the air and the glass, because it is able to travel through them. If it hits the glass at an angle, it will be refracted (or bent) as it passes into and out of the glass. Some of the light might also be reflected by the glass. The light is absorbed by the person's eye.

Know

1 What happens when light hits an object and is:

   a) absorbed

   b) transmitted

   c) reflected

   d) refracted?

2 Which of the four options in question 1 do the following diagrams show?

   a) 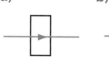 **b)**   **c)**   **d)**

3 What is the law of reflection?

4 Copy the diagram below, then label it with the following keywords:

   a) Ray box   **e)** Reflected ray

   b) Mirror   **f)** Angle of incidence (i)

   c) Normal   **g)** Angle of reflection (r)

   d) Incident ray

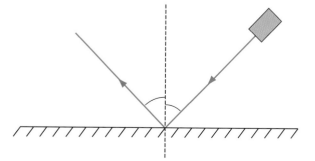

5 If the angle of incidence was 30 degrees, what would the angle of reflection be?

6 If the angle of reflection was 45 degrees, what would the angle of incidence be?

7 What is refraction? When does it happen?

Apply

1 What's wrong with the following ray diagrams of reflection? Describe how it should be corrected.

a)   b)   c)   d)

2 Make a copy of the diagram on the right. Add in two light rays to show how the eye would see the apple reflected in the mirror.

3 Copy the diagram below, then label it with the following keywords:

a) Glass block

b) Normal (×2)

c) Incident ray

d) Refracted ray

e) Angle of incidence (×2)

f) Angle of refraction (×2)

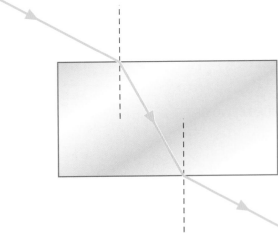

> **Hint**
>
> Light rays travel into the eye when we see things, not out of it.

4 Copy out the sentences below, leaving out the incorrect words.

a) When light travels from a less dense to a denser medium, it bends *towards/away from* the normal.

b) When light travels from a denser to a less dense medium, it bends *towards/away from* the normal.

c) Light doesn't refract if it enters a new medium at *0/90* degrees.

» Colours

Worked example

White light travels through two filters; the first is magenta and the second is red.

a) What colour(s) of light are transmitted through this combination?
b) What colour would a white T-shirt, red jumper and blue pair of jeans look through these filters?

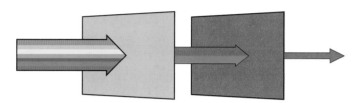

a) The magenta filter absorbs all light that is not blue or red. The red filter then absorbs the blue light and only allows the red light to be transmitted.
b) Under the remaining red light, a white T-shirt would look red, as would the red jumper. The blue jeans would look black, as blue objects absorb all colours of light except blue, which they reflect.

> **Hint**
>
> A white object reflects all colours of light. A black object reflects none. A coloured object (e.g. red) reflects only that colour, and absorbs the rest.

Know

1 Describe the difference between transparent, translucent and opaque materials and state an example of each.

2 What is scattering?

3 What is a luminous object?

4 Copy and complete this diagram by filling in the colours of the spectrum.

5 What are the three primary colours of light?

Apply

1 Copy and complete the colour chart on the right to show how light can be combined to make different colours.

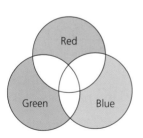

2 Copy and complete the table below to show which colours of light the filters will let through.

Filter colour	Will this filter transmit...		
	...blue light?	...red light?	...green light?
Blue			
Red			
Green			
Yellow			
Cyan			
Magenta			

9 Particle model

» Model of solids, liquids and gases

Worked example

Explain, using the particle model, why a solid bar of iron expands when it is heated.

The iron particles gain energy and vibrate more vigorously. As a result the particles move further apart.

Know

1 How are the particles arranged in:

   a) a solid

   b) a liquid

   c) a gas?

2 Describe how the movement of the water particles differs between ice, water and water vapour.

3 The diagram shows the three states of matter for a substance.

   Each circle represents a particle of the substance.

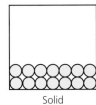  

      Solid   Liquid   Gas

   a) Copy and complete the diagram by drawing three circles to represent the particles of a gas.

   b) Which statement is correct about the movement or arrangement of the particles of this substance?

      A They move randomly in the liquid state.

      B They move randomly in the solid state.

      C They are arranged in fixed positions in the gas state.

      D They are arranged in fixed positions in the liquid state.

c) Which word describes the change that takes place when a solid becomes a liquid?

    A boiling

    B condensing

    C freezing

    D melting

Apply

1 The diagram shows the arrangement of the particles in a solid, a liquid and a gas.

    Solid   Liquid   Gas

Explain each of the following statements using the particle model of solids, liquids and gases.

a) A liquid cannot be easily compressed.

b) A gas occupies all of the container in which it is placed.

c) A solid is usually more dense than its liquid.

d) A solid cannot flow, but a liquid can flow.

» Changes of state

Worked example

Iron has a melting point of 1535 °C and a boiling point of 3000 °C. Work out what state iron is in at each of the following temperatures: 1600 °C, 200 °C, 3200 °C.

At 1600 °C the iron is above its melting point but below its boiling point, so it is a liquid.
At 200 °C the iron is below its melting point, so it is a solid.
At 3200 °C the iron is above its boiling point, so it is a gas.

Know

1 When solid iodine is heated it changes directly into iodine gas. What name is given to this process?

    A condensation

    B diffusion

    C evaporation

    D sublimation

2 The table below shows the melting and boiling points of four elements, A, B, C and D.

Element	Melting point in °C	Boiling point in °C
A	660	2520
B	1540	2760
C	650	1100
D	−39	357

Which element in the table is:

a) a liquid at 0 °C

b) a solid at 1500 °C

c) a gas at 500 °C

d) a liquid over the biggest temperature range?

Apply

1 Some cold water is poured into a flask and a bung is inserted. The diagram shows the flask after a few minutes.

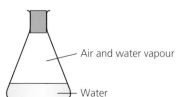

Air and water vapour

Water

a) Use the particle model to explain how water vapour becomes mixed with the air in the flask.

b) What is the name given to the process in which water becomes water vapour?

2 In a kettle water is boiled to form steam. The steam then cools to form water droplets. State the change in:

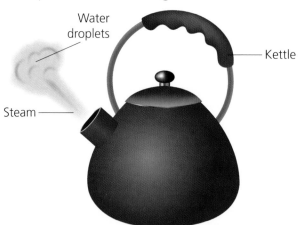

Water droplets

Kettle

Steam

a) energy

b) arrangement

c) movement of the water particles

as the steam cools to form liquid water.

3 Ice melts at 0 °C. Sulfur melts at 113 °C. Explain whether the forces of attraction between the particles in ice are stronger, weaker or just the same as the forces of attraction between the sulfur particles in solid sulfur.

4 Use the particle model to explain what happens to the particles of water when it boils to form steam.

» Sublimation, diffusion and pressure

Worked example

Use the particle model to explain how air inside a balloon creates pressure on the sides of the balloon. Why does the pressure increase if you blow more air into the balloon?

The air particles are continually colliding with each other and with the sides of the balloon. When a particle collides with the wall, it exerts a small force on the wall. The pressure exerted by the air is a result of the collision forces of all of the particles.
When you blow more air into the balloon, you add more particles. The more particles that hit the walls, the higher the pressure.

Know

1 What is the name of the process that occurs when a solid changes straight into a gas?

  A condensation

  B diffusion

  C evaporation

  D sublimation

2 What is the name of the process when the gas spreads out to fill the gas jar?

  A condensation

  B diffusion

  C evaporation

  D sublimation

Apply

1 A large crystal of the purple compound potassium permanganate is added to water in a beaker. After 1 week the crystal of potassium permanganate is much smaller and the whole of the liquid is purple. Use the particle model to explain these observations.

2 Explain why diffusion takes place much more slowly in a liquid than in a gas.

3 A small amount of liquid bromine is placed into a sealed jar that contains air. After 2 minutes a brown gas is seen just above the surface of the liquid. After 2 hours the whole jar is full of a brown gas.

  Explain the observations using the particle model.

10 Separating mixtures

» Pure substances and mixtures

Worked example

Hydrated copper sulfate is a blue solid that is soluble in water. Lead carbonate is a white solid that is insoluble in water. Describe and explain what you would see if a small sample of each of these solids was added separately to water, and the mixture was stirred.

When the copper sulfate is added to water and stirred, the blue solid disappears and the water turns blue. The copper sulfate dissolves. The particles of copper sulfate have broken away from the solid and have spread evenly throughout the water.

When lead carbonate is added to water and stirred, the white solid does not disappear and the water goes cloudy white. The lead carbonate does not dissolve. The particles of lead carbonate remain joined together in each of the small lumps of the solid lead carbonate.

> **Hint**
> When answering a question that asks for both a description and an explanation, give the description first and then give the explanation in a separate sentence.

Know

1 When sugar is added to water and the mixture is stirred, the sugar disappears. A possible explanation for this is that the sugar _____ in water.

Choose from the list a word that best fills the gap in the paragraph above.

A condenses **B** dissolves **C** evaporates **D** melts

2 State whether each of the following is a pure substance or a mixture of substances.

a) air

d) mineral water

b) iron

e) sea water

c) sodium chloride

3 Some salt is added to water. The mixture is stirred and the salt dissolves. Choose a word from the box to complete the sentences that follow.

solute	solvent	solution

a) The salt is the _____.

b) The water is the _____.

c) The mixture of salt and water is a _____.

Apply

1 Salol is a solid that melts at 42 °C to form liquid salol. Liquid salol and a solution of salol are both colourless liquids.

   a) What is the difference between liquid salol and a solution of salol?

   b) How would you obtain solid salol from a solution of salol?

   c) How would you obtain solid salol from liquid salol?

2 Tincture of iodine is a mixture of solid iodine dissolved in liquid alcohol. Give the name of:

   a) the solvent

   b) the solute

   in tincture of iodine.

» Purifying liquids

Worked example

Coffee can be made from ground coffee by placing the ground coffee in a paper filter and pouring hot water onto the coffee. The solution of coffee can then be collected in a jug placed below the filter.

a) Why is hot water used rather than cold water?
b) Why is a filter used?
c) Why is it not necessary to use a filter when you make instant coffee?

a) The coffee will dissolve more quickly in hot water than in cold water.
b) To remove the substances that do not dissolve in water.
c) Instant coffee contains only substances that are soluble in water. The insoluble substances have been removed.

Know

1 Complete each of the following sentences using words from the box.

gas	liquid	solid	solution

   a) Filtration is used to separate an insoluble solid from a _____.

   b) Evaporation is used to separate a soluble solid from a _____.

   c) Distillation is used to separate a _____ from a solution.

2 Chalk does not dissolve in water, but sugar does. A mixture of chalk and sugar is added to water and the mixture is stirred. The mixture is then filtered using a filter funnel and paper.

   a) Which substance remains in the filter paper after filtration?

   b) What does the liquid that passes through the filter paper consist of?

   c) The liquid that passes through the filter paper is left in a warm place. After 2 days all that is left is a white solid. What is the white solid?

3 Salt is soluble in water. Sand is insoluble in water. This difference allows a mixture of salt and sand to be separated using the apparatus shown in the diagram.

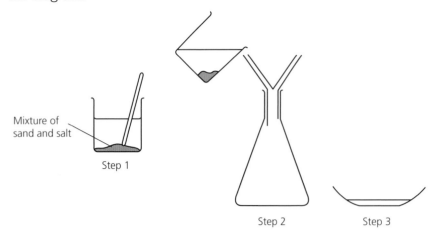

Mixture of sand and salt

Step 1

Step 2

Step 3

Use terms from the box to complete the following sentences. Each term may be used once, more than once, or not at all.

beaker	Bunsen burner	conical flask	glass rod
thermometer	water	filter funnel	

a) In Step 1, the mixture of salt and sand is put into a _____ containing _____ and the mixture is stirred with a _____.

b) In Step 2, the mixture is poured through a _____ into a _____.

c) In Step 3, the liquid from Step 2 is put into a basin to allow the _____ to evaporate.

Apply

1 Rock salt contains a mixture of sand, dirt and salt. Both sand and dirt are insoluble in water. Salt is soluble in water. Describe how you could separate and collect the salt from rock salt.

2 You have spilt some sugar into a packet of rice grains. Describe how you could obtain the rice from the mixture.

3 Four methods that can be used to separate substances in a mixture are:

- chromatography
- distillation
- evaporation
- filtration.

Choose the best method to:

a) obtain water from a solution of solid copper sulfate dissolved in water

b) obtain solid salt from a solution of salt in water

c) obtain solid chalk from a suspension of chalk in water

d) separate the coloured materials in a food dye.

4 The diagram shows the apparatus that is used to obtain a liquid from a solution of a solid dissolved in the liquid

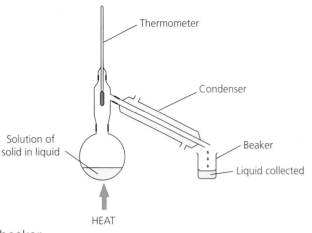

Thermometer

Condenser

Solution of solid in liquid

Beaker

Liquid collected

HEAT

a) What is the name given to this method of separation?

b) A student uses this apparatus to obtain a liquid from sea water.

   i) What will be the temperature reading on the thermometer as the liquid is being collected in the beaker?

   ii) Give the name of the liquid collected in the beaker.

   iii) Explain how this method of separation works.

» Chromatography

Worked example

A lime-flavoured ice-lolly is coloured green. State how you would show whether the ice-lolly contained a single green colouring or a mixture of yellow and blue colourings.

Allow the lolly to melt and then carry out chromatography on the liquid. If there is only a single green colouring present then there will be a single spot on the paper. If there is a mixture of yellow and blue, then there will be two spots on the paper. One will be coloured yellow, the other coloured blue.

> **Hint**
>
> The question does not ask for experimental details, so all that is necessary is to state the name of the method that should be used. Also, it is important to give the expected result if there is only a single colouring present, and if there is a mixture present.

Know

1 State what is meant by the term chromatography.

Apply

1 The diagram shows the result of an experiment to separate the colours present in four different dyes, P, Q, R and S.

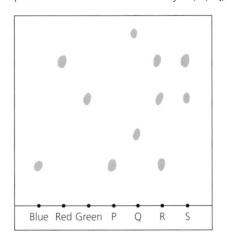

Blue   Red   Green   P   Q   R   S

a) State and explain which dye contains three colours.

b) Each dye is made from one or more of the colours blue, red and green. State and explain which one of the results appears to be incorrect.

11 Metals and non-metals

» Metals

Worked example

Boron is an element with a very high melting point. It is a poor conductor of both electricity and heat, and it is also brittle.

Suggest whether boron is a metal or a non-metal. Explain your answer.

Boron is probably a non-metal. This is because it is a poor conductor of both electricity and heat – both properties of non-metals. The high melting point is of no use in deciding, because some non-metals (e.g. carbon) and most metals have high melting points.

Know

1 State what is meant by each of the following terms:

   a) malleable   b) ductile   c) brittle.

2 The following is a list of elements: calcium, carbon, copper, mercury, sulfur, iron, aluminium, bromine. State which elements are metals and which are non-metals.

3 a) Give the names of the two elements that are liquids at room temperature (20 °C).

   b) Which of these two elements is a metal and which is a non-metal?

4 Which of the following lists contains three magnetic elements?

   A gold, iron and zinc   C aluminium, cobalt and silver

   B cobalt, iron and nickel   D iron, nickel and tin

Apply

1 The table contains descriptions of five elements, A, B, C, D and E.

Element	Description
A	A colourless gas that burns in air to form a liquid oxide.
B	A shiny solid that forms a black oxide. The oxide is basic and is insoluble in water.
C	A liquid that is a good conductor of heat.
D	A yellow solid that is a poor conductor of electricity and that forms an acidic oxide.
E	A shiny solid that is a good conductor of electricity. It is not very reactive.

   a) Classify each of the elements as a metal or a non-metal. Give reasons for your answers.

   b) Suggest a possible identity for each element.

2 A student found a lump of a yellow solid. He thought it might be either sulfur or gold. The table lists some properties of sulfur and gold.

Sulfur	Gold
Poor conductor of electricity	Good conductor of electricity
Poor conductor of heat	Good conductor of heat
Melting point 113 °C	Melting point 1063 °C
Burns when heated in air	Does not burn when heated in air
Brittle	Malleable

a) What can the student deduce from each of the following tests carried out on the yellow lump?

   i)   It did not conduct electricity.

   ii) It did not melt when heated to 1500 °C with a Bunsen burner.

   iii) It did not burn when heated in air.

   iv) It broke into pieces when hit with a hammer.

b) Could the yellow solid be either sulfur or gold? Explain your answer.

3 The diagrams show the reactions of some metals with water and with dilute sulfuric acid.

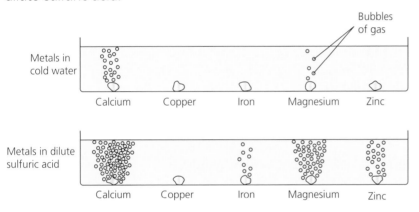

Use the diagrams to answer the following questions.

a) Name two metals that react with cold water.

b) Name one metal that reacts with dilute sulfuric acid but not with water.

c) Arrange the metals in order of reactivity. Place the most reactive metal first.

» Metals, acids and the reactivity series

Worked example

When a mixture of black copper oxide and black carbon is heated in a test tube, a pink-brown solid is formed.

a) Identify the pink-brown solid.
b) Write a word equation for the reaction.
c) Explain which element, copper or carbon, is the more reactive.
d) When this reaction takes place on a crucible lid, very little of the pink-brown solid can be seen. Explain why.

a) Copper

b) copper oxide + carbon → copper + carbon dioxide

c) Carbon is the more reactive element because it displaces copper from copper oxide.

d) Oxygen from the air reacts with the copper to reform copper oxide.

Know

1 Which of the following word equations represents the reaction between zinc and sulfuric acid?

A zinc + sulfuric acid → zinc sulfate + hydrogen

B zinc + sulfuric acid → zinc sulfide + hydrogen

C zinc + sulfuric acid → zinc sulfate + water

D zinc + sulfuric acid → zinc sulfide + water

Apply

1 A student observes the reaction of dilute sulfuric acid with four metals, W, X, Y and Z. The table shows her observations.

Metal	Observations
W	Few bubbles produced slowly
X	Many bubbles produced quickly
Y	Many bubbles produced very quickly
Z	Very few bubbles produced very slowly

a) Use the information in the table to place the four metals in order of reactivity. Place the most reactive metal first.

b) The gas given off when a metal reacts with sulfuric acid is hydrogen. Describe a test to show that the gas is hydrogen.

2 Three metals X, Y and Z are added to separate samples of hydrochloric acid. The volume of hydrogen given off is measured. The graphs show the results obtained.

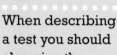

Hint

When describing a test you should also give the result of the test if positive.

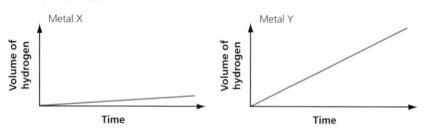
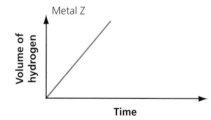

a) Which metal produced hydrogen most quickly?

b) Which metal produced hydrogen least quickly?

c) Put the three metals in order of reactivity. Put the most reactive first.

d) What variables should you control in order to make this a fair test.

REACTIONS

» How do metals and non-metals react with oxygen?

Worked example

When a piece of burning calcium is lowered into a gas jar containing carbon dioxide gas, the calcium continues to burn. A white solid and a black solid are formed. Explain these observations.

The calcium reacts with the carbon dioxide forming calcium oxide, a white solid, and carbon (a black solid). The reaction takes place because calcium is more reactive than carbon.

Know

1   What is the name of the reaction in which an element combines with oxygen to form an oxide?

   A displacement   **C** oxidation

   B neutralisation   **D** reduction

2   State what is seen when a piece of magnesium ribbon is burned in oxygen.

Apply

1   Nickel does not react with zinc oxide when heated together. Nickel reacts with lead oxide when heated together to form nickel oxide and lead.

   a) Place the elements lead, nickel and zinc in order of their reactivity. Place the most reactive first.

   b) Explain what reaction, if any, will take place when:

   i)   a mixture of lead and nickel oxide is heated

   ii) a mixture of zinc and nickel oxide is heated.

2   Sapphires are made of an aluminium compound with the formula Al_2O_3. The chemical symbol for aluminium is Al.

   a) i)   Give the name of the other element combined with aluminium in this compound.

   ii) Suggest the name of the compound with the formula Al_2O_3.

Sapphires are often mounted in gold to make rings. Gold is an element found in rocks. Gold is hardly ever found combined with other elements. Part of the reactivity series is shown here:

Most reactive	Aluminium
	Zinc
	Iron
	Lead
Least reactive	Copper

   b) Suggest where gold should be placed in this reactivity series.

» Displacement reactions

Worked example

Iron displaces copper from a solution of copper sulfate. Magnesium displaces iron from a solution of iron sulfate. Write a word equation for each of these two reactions and put the metals in order of reactivity (i.e. most reactive first).

iron + copper sulfate → iron sulfate + copper
magnesium + iron sulfate → magnesium sulfate + iron
magnesium > iron > copper

Know

1 What is the name of the reaction in which a metal takes the place of a less reactive metal in a compound?

   A displacement

   B neutralisation

   C oxidation

   D reduction

Apply

1 Use information from the table below to answer the questions that follow.

Increasing reactivity	Metal	Colour of solid metal	Colour of a solution of the metal sulfate
	Magnesium	Grey	Colourless
	Zinc	Grey	Colourless
	Iron	Dark grey	Green
	Copper	Pink-brown	Blue

a) Explain why no reaction occurs when zinc is added to magnesium sulfate solution.

b) When powdered iron is added to copper sulfate solution, a reaction takes place.

   i) Write a word equation for this reaction.

   ii) Describe the colour changes that occur during this reaction.

       Colour of solid changes from _____ to _____.

       Colour of solution changes from _____ to _____.

c) When copper is added to dilute sulfuric acid, no reaction occurs. When iron is added to dilute sulfuric acid, iron sulfate and hydrogen are formed. What does this suggest about the reactivity of hydrogen compared with the reactivity of copper and the reactivity of iron?

12 Acids and alkalis

≫ The pH scale

Worked example

A solution has a pH of 6. What does this tell you about the solution?

A solution with a pH of 6 is weakly acidic.

Know

1 Sulfuric acid is a strong acid. Citric acid is a weak acid. Sodium chloride is a neutral salt. Suggest a pH value for a dilute solution of each.

2 Give the chemical formula for each of the following acids and alkalis:

   a) hydrochloric acid

   b) sodium hydroxide

   c) sulfuric acid

   d) potassium hydroxide

   e) nitric acid

   f) calcium hydroxide

3 The pH of a solution can be measured using a pH meter. Describe one other method to measure the pH of a solution.

4 Which of the following statements about bases is true?

   A They are all alkalis.

   B They can neutralise acids.

   C They are all soluble in water.

   D They react with an acid to produce hydrogen.

Apply

1 An acidic solution and an alkaline solution were mixed together in the volumes shown in the table.

Volume of acidic solution in cm^3	Volume of alkaline solution in cm^3	pH of mixture
25	15	
25	17	
25	19	

One mixture had a pH of 7, one had a pH of 2 and one had a pH of 12. Copy the table and complete the third column.

2 Four test tubes contain dilute solutions of hydrochloric acid (strongly acidic), sodium chloride (neutral), vinegar (weakly acidic) and washing soda (strongly alkaline). You do not know which test tube contains which solution, so you add a few drops of universal indicator to each tube. The table shows your results.

Test tube	Colour	pH
A	Red	1
B	Yellow	6
C	Green	7
D	Blue	11

Use the results to identify each solution.

3 The first table below shows the colour of universal indicator in acidic, neutral and alkaline solutions.

	Acidic			Neutral		Alkaline	
Colour of indicator	Red	Orange	Yellow	Green	Light blue	Dark blue	Purple

This next table shows the results of testing different solutions with the indicator.

Solution	Colour of indicator
Oven cleaner	Purple
Milk	Green
Lemonade	Orange
Mineral water	Light blue
Lemon juice	Red

a) Give the name of an acidic solution in the second table.

b) Give the name of a strongly alkaline solution in the second table.

c) Give the name of a neutral solution in the second table.

4 A student wants to test the theory that the colour of the petals of a hydrangea plant depends on the pH of the soil in which it is planted. She measures the pH of five different soils, A, B, C, D and E and records the colour of the hydrangeas planted in them. The table shows her results.

Soil	pH of soil	Colour of petals
A	4.5	Blue
B	5.5	Violet
C	6.5	Violet
D	7.0	Light pink
E	7.5	Dark pink

a) Describe how the student could measure the pH of a dry sample of soil.

b) Explain whether the results support the statement that the colour of the petals depends on the pH of the soil.

» Acids reacting with alkalis

Worked example

An old memory aid for treating bee and wasp stings is '**B**ee – **B**icarb'; '**V**inegar – **V**asp'. 'Bicarb' is sodium hydrogencarbonate, a weak alkali. Vinegar is a weak acid.

What do these treatments suggest about the nature of bee and wasp stings? Justify your answer.

Bee stings may be acidic and wasp stings may be alkaline. This is assuming that the remedy involves a neutralisation reaction. The alkaline sodium hydrogencarbonate will neutralise the acid in the bee sting, while the acidic vinegar will neutralise the alkali in the wasp sting.

Know

1 What is the name of the type of reaction that takes place when an acid reacts with an alkali?

  A displacement   C oxidation

  B neutralisation   D reduction

2 State what is meant by the term indicator.

3 What is the colour of methyl orange in acidic solutions and in alkaline solutions?

Apply

1 The diagram shows part of the pH scale.

pH 0- -7- -14
Strongly acidic   Neutral   Strongly alkaline
   solution   solution

Some of these experiments involve a pH change.

  A Carbon dioxide gas is dissolved in pure water.

  B Excess sodium hydroxide solution is added to a weakly acidic solution.

  C Sodium hydroxide solution is neutralised by adding citric acid.

  D Sodium chloride (common salt) is dissolved in pure water.

  E Hydrochloric acid is added to pure water.

The table shows the pH at the start and at the end of each of the five experiments. Copy and complete the table by inserting the appropriate letter in each box. The first one has been done for you.

pH at start	pH at end	Experiment
5	14	B
7	6	
7	7	
7	1	
14	7	

» Acids reacting with metal carbonates

Worked example

Write a word equation for the reaction between copper carbonate and nitric acid.

copper carbonate + nitric acid → copper nitrate + water + carbon dioxide

Know

1 What is the name of the gas produced when an acid reacts with a carbonate?

2 What products are formed when an acid reacts with a metal carbonate?

    A a salt only   C a salt and hydrogen

    B a salt, carbon dioxide and water   D a salt and water

3 Which of the following is the test for carbon dioxide?

    A It produces a pop when ignited.   C It turns damp red litmus blue.

    B It relights a glowing splint.   D It turns limewater milky.

Apply

1 The word equation for the reaction between zinc carbonate and dilute nitric acid is shown below:

zinc carbonate + nitric acid → zinc nitrate + carbon dioxide + water

The apparatus below is used to investigate this reaction.

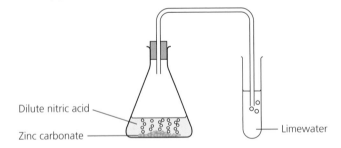

Dilute nitric acid

Zinc carbonate

Limewater

    a) Suggest a pH value for dilute nitric acid.

    b) What change do you observe in the limewater as the carbon dioxide bubbles through it?

    c) At the end of the reaction all of the nitric acid has been used up.

       Suggest a value for the pH of the remaining solution.

2 A student collected two different samples of rainwater and measured the pH of each sample. The table shows his results.

Sample	Where collected	pH
A	Rainwater collected as it fell from the sky	5.6
B	Rainwater collected after it had passed through limestone rocks	6.7

a) Which of the following statements about rainwater is true?

    A It is strongly acidic.

    B It is weakly acidic.

    C It is strongly alkaline.

    D It is weakly alkaline.

b) What kind of reaction occurs when rainwater passes through limestone rock?

c) When nitric acid is added to limestone rock, calcium nitrate and carbon dioxide are both produced. Name the chemical compound that must be present in the limestone rock.

13 Earth structure

» The structure of the Earth

Worked example

Feldspars make up approximately 60% of the Earth's crust. One type of feldspar has the formula $KAlSi_3O_8$. Is this feldspar a mineral or a rock? Explain your answer.

It is a mineral since it has a definite chemical formula.

Know

1 Describe each of the following parts of the Earth:

   a) the core   b) the mantle   c) the crust.

2 What is the difference between most rocks and a mineral?

3 Why is coal not classed as a mineral?

Apply

1 A student is comparing the hardness of five rocks. These are her results.

   • Rock A makes rock C crumble.   • Rock C makes rock D crumble.

   • Rock B makes rock A crumble.   • Rock E makes rock B crumble.

   Arrange the rocks in order of hardness. Put the hardest rock first.

» Types of rock

Worked example

The diagram shows an arrangement of rock layers in which three different types of rock, A, B and C, are present.

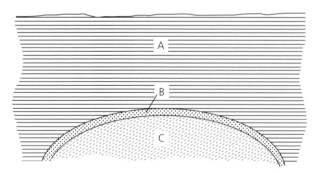

One rock is igneous (granite), another is metamorphic (quartzite) and the third is sedimentary (sandstone).

a) Use the information above to state which of the rocks is granite, which is quartzite and which is sandstone.

b) Describe how quartzite is formed.

a) A is sandstone; B is quartzite; C is granite
b) The action of heat and pressure on the sandstone.

Know

1 a) State what is meant by the following terms:

    i) sedimentary rock

    ii) igneous rock

    iii) metamorphic rock.

b) Give an example of each type of rock listed in part a.

2 The diagram shows the remains of a plant that lived millions of years ago.

Use words from the box to complete the sentences below.

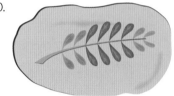

fossils   igneous   metamorphic   sedimentary   soil

a) The remains of the plant are called _____ .

b) The remains of plants are found in _____ rocks.

c) Weathering can break down rocks to form _____ .

Apply

1 a) Explain how fossils were formed.

b) Explain why fossils are not found in igneous or metamorphic rock.

c) Explain why very few fossils are found of creatures with soft bodies.

2 The diagrams show three fossils commonly found in different layers of sedimentary rock.

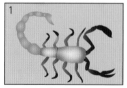 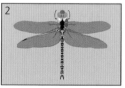 

  280 million years ago   345 million years ago   430 million years ago

a) Describe how sedimentary rocks are formed.

b) Why are sedimentary rocks formed in layers?

The diagram on the right shows a sample of six layers of sedimentary rock.

c) Fossil 2 above was found in layer E of the sample. In which layer might you expect to find fossil 3? Give a reason for your answer.

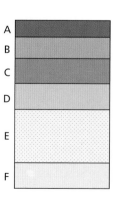

» The rock cycle

Worked example

Weathering of limestone carvings leaves them pitted and worn away. The weathering is caused by the action of acid rain. Is this an example of chemical or physical weathering? Explain your answer.

Chemical weathering. The acid in the rain reacts with the limestone.

> **Hint**
>
> Chemical weathering involves a chemical reaction, whereas physical weathering does not.

Know

1 What is the difference between weathering and erosion?

2 What type of weathering is caused by the action of running water on rocks in streams or rivers?

Apply

1 **a)** State two ways in which rocks are broken down by weathering.

   b) After rocks have been broken down, the particles are sometimes carried away by natural processes.

       i)   What name is given to the process in which the particles are carried away?

       ii) State one way in which the particles may be carried away.

   c) Which of the following rocks has been formed by the action of heat and pressure?

       A chalk   **C** limestone

       B granite   **D** marble

2 The diagram shows a rock being weathered until it eventually becomes rounded.

A   B   C

   a) Suggest two different ways in which the rock has become rounded.

   b) Suggest a place where rock C is most likely to be found. Give a reason for your answer.

3 The diagram below is a sketch of a quarry face.

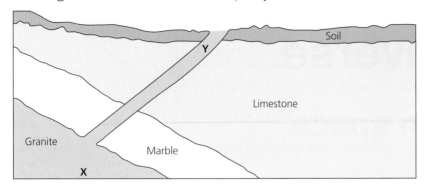

a) The limestone was originally formed in layers. State what type of rock limestone is.

b) Granite is an igneous rock formed from magma.

   i) Explain how the marble has formed above the granite.

   ii) Explain why the rock at Y contains smaller crystals than the rock at X.

4 The diagram shows different rock types found on an island as it was many years ago and as it is today.

Island many years ago

Island today

a) The diagram shows that rock A used to cover the top of the island. Copy and complete the paragraph that explains why the layer of rock A has changed. Choose words from this list:

erosion	transported	weathered	water

Wind and _____ have _____ rock A, breaking it into small pieces. The small pieces have then been _____ away by water and wind. This is called _____.

b) Rock B is igneous rock.

   i) How is igneous rock formed?

   ii) Rock B was made of large crystals. What does this tell you about the way the rock was formed?

c) Rock C was formed from rock B by heating and pressure. What name is given to rock that is changed by heating and pressure?

14 Universe

» The Earth in space

Worked example

Why, on Earth, does the Sun rise in the east and set in the west?

It is because the Earth spins towards the east.

Know

1 State, in terms of the Earth's movement, what is meant by each of the following terms.

   a) an orbit   **b)** a year   **c)** a day

2 How long does it take for light to reach the Earth from:

   a) the Sun

   b) the Earth's next nearest star?

   c) Give the name of the galaxy that contains our solar system.

Apply

1 **a)** Spacecraft containing astronauts have reached the Moon but have so far not reached Mars. One reason for this is that:

   A the Moon is closer to the Earth than Mars

   B the Moon is closer to the Sun than Mars

   C Mars is closer to the Earth than the Moon

   D Mars is closer to the Sun than the Moon.

   b) Which of these objects in space is the smallest?

   A Earth   **C** the Moon

   B Jupiter   **D** the Sun

» The solar system

Worked example

Pluto spins on its axis in the opposite direction from the Earth. What effect would this have on an observation made on Pluto of the Sun's movement?

The Sun will rise in the west and set in the east.

Know

1 The diagram shows four moons that orbit Jupiter.

a) Jupiter is:

    A a comet   **C** a planet

    B a galaxy   **D** a universe.

b) Galileo used a new invention to observe these moons. Give the name of the invention he used.

Apply

1 Quaoar is a large asteroid orbiting the Sun. The diagram shows Quaoar in four positions in its orbit.

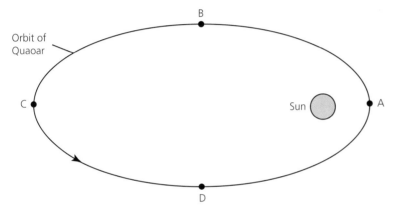

a) In which of the four positions, A, B, C or D, is the effect of the Sun's gravity greatest? Explain your answer.

b) In which of the four positions, A, B, C or D, is Quaoar travelling most slowly. Explain your answer.

c) The table below gives some information about three planets in our solar system.

Planet	Average distance from the Sun (in millions of km)	Time for one orbit of the Sun (in Earth years)	Average surface temperature of planet (in °C)
Jupiter	789	12	−153
Saturn	1427	30	−185
Neptune	4497	165	−225

    i) The time for one orbit of Uranus is 84 Earth years. Estimate the average distance of Uranus from the Sun.

    ii) How does the surface temperature of these planets vary with distance from the Sun?

    iii) Explain why the surface temperature varies with distance from the Sun.

2 The diagram shows part of the solar system.

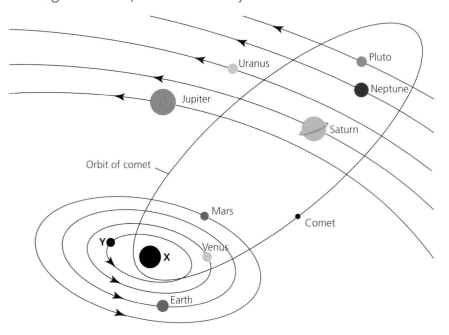

a) Give the names of X and Y.

b) Give two reasons why it takes Jupiter longer than Mars to complete one orbit around the Sun.

c) The diagram also shows the orbit of a comet. A comet was seen from Earth in 1531, 1607 and 1682.

    i) Suggest why the comet that was seen was probably the same one each time.

    ii) The comet was last seen in 1986. Predict when it will next be seen.

3 The diagram below shows the solar system as drawn by Ptolemy over 2000 years ago.

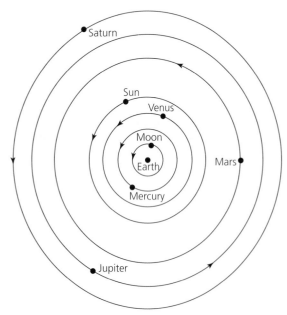

a) Suggest why Ptolemy did not include the planets Uranus and Neptune in his diagram.

b) Give two ways in which Ptolemy's solar system is different from the one we draw today.

4 The diagram shows the solar system.

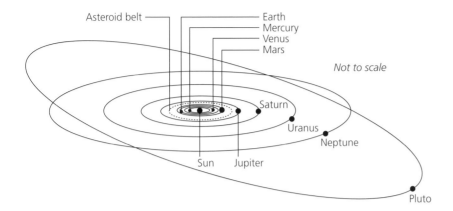

Asteroid belt — Earth — Mercury — Venus — Mars — *Not to scale* — Saturn — Uranus — Neptune — Sun — Jupiter — Pluto

a) i) How does the length of a 'year' on Neptune differ from a 'year' on Earth?

ii) Explain your answer.

b) i) What is the name of the force that keeps the planets in orbit around the Sun?

ii) How does the size of this force change as the distance between a planet and the Sun increases?

» Phases of the Moon

Worked example

The image shows a solar eclipse. A solar eclipse occurs when the Moon passes between the Sun and the Earth.

a) The Moon is much smaller than the Sun. Which one of the following explains why the Moon appears to be about the same size as the Sun during a solar eclipse?

  A The Moon is closer to the Earth than the Sun is.

  B The Sun is closer to the Earth than the Moon is.

  C The Moon goes around the Earth much faster than the Sun does.

  D The Sun goes around the Earth much faster than the Moon does.

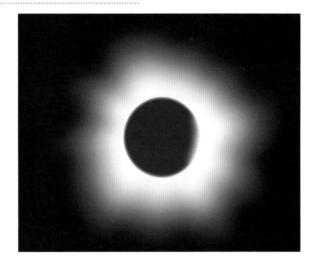

b) The graph below shows how the light levels changed during the eclipse.

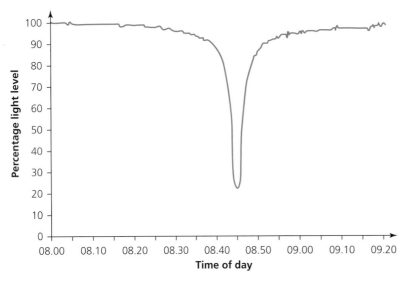

i) At what time of day did the Moon block out most of the Sun's light?

ii) Suggest what happens to the temperature of the air during the eclipse. Give a reason for your answer.

a) A (The Moon is closer to the Earth than the Sun is)

b) i) 08.45

ii) The temperature drops because the Moon blocks out the heat from the Sun.

Know

1 The Moon does not give off light, so why can it be seen from the Earth?

2 What is the name given to the plane of the Earth's orbit around the Sun?

Apply

1 The diagram shows the eight-phase lunar cycle.

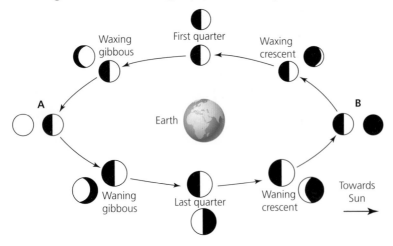

What name is given to the moon at point A and at point B?

» Beyond the solar system

Worked example

The distance from Earth to Alpha Centauri is 41 340 000 000 000 km. How long does it take for light from Alpha Centauri to reach Earth?
[The speed of light is 300 000 km/s]

time = distance/speed
= 41 340 000 000 000 km/300 000 km/s
= 137 800 000 s

(This is equivalent to 4.37 years – there are 31 536 000 seconds in one year. This means that as we look at Alpha Centauri, we are seeing it as it was 4.37 years ago, not as it is today.)

> **Hint** !
>
> To calculate time you need to rearrange the equation 'distance = speed × time'.

Know

1 State what is meant by each of the following terms:

   a) a galaxy

   b) a light year

   c) a star.

2 **a)** A galaxy is a collection of:

   A asteroids   **C** planets

   B moons   **D** stars.

   b) Andromeda is just one of the many galaxies that form the:

   A constellations   **C** stars

   B planets   **D** universe.

Apply

1 Scientists use telescopes to search for new planets orbiting distant stars. The Kepler space telescope orbits above the Earth's atmosphere and records the brightness of light from distant stars. When a planet passes in front of a distant star, there is a tiny dip in the brightness of the light from the star.

   a) Suggest why telescopes that search for planets orbiting distant stars are not on the Earth's surface.

   b) The Kepler telescope was pointed towards one star. It detected the same dip in the brightness of the star every 150 days. Suggest what information this gives about the planet that orbits this star.

15 Movement

» The seven life processes

Worked example

Cars share some characteristics with living organisms, but they are definitely not living. Describe *and* explain which of the seven life processes cars show.

A car does:
- <u>movement</u> – it has wheels and an engine that move it from one place to another
- <u>nutrition</u> – it consumes fuel in order to move
- <u>respiration</u> – it burns the fuel in the engine to release energy to make the car move
- <u>excretion</u> – the exhaust pipe releases exhaust gases.

Many modern cars are also <u>sensitive</u> – they can respond to their environment using sensors and computer software.

Hint

In this question, 'describe and explain' means say what each characteristic is (describe it), and then show how a car displays this characteristic (explain).

Know

1 Copy and complete the following paragraph using your knowledge of the seven life processes:

All living organisms carry out seven life processes. We can remember them using 'MRS NERG': 'M' stands for _____, 'R' stands for _____, 'S' stands for _____, 'N' stands for _____, 'E' stands for _____, 'R' stands for _____ and 'G' stands for _____.

Hint

A common mistake students make is to think that respiration means 'breathing'. Respiration is not breathing – it is a chemical reaction that releases energy.

Apply

1 Which of the seven life processes is to do with:

a) removing waste products from a living organism

b) converting particles from food into useable energy

c) producing other living organisms

d) absorbing substances to help the organism stay alive

e) responding to the surrounding environment

f) changing the position of the organism

g) the physical development of the organism?

2 Plants are definitely living organisms.

   a) Give an example of how a plant might move by itself.

   b) Give an example of a part of a plant involved in reproduction.

   c) How do sunflowers show that they are sensitive to the environment around them?

» Skeletons

Worked example

Explain why, in humans, the pelvis of a woman tends to be wider than the pelvis of a man.

Because a wide pelvis makes it easier for a baby to be born as the baby has to be born through the pelvis. Men do not get pregnant and give birth, so they don't benefit from having a wider pelvis.

> **Hint**
>
> When answering an 'explain' question, the word 'because' is really useful because it shows you are explaining.

Know

1 Give the four functions of a skeleton.

2 What is the name of an area where two bones of a skeleton meet?

3 Skeletons and muscles allow animals to move. What is the name of the substance that joins muscles to bones?

4 Give the name of the part of some bones where blood cells are formed.

5 Calcium and phosphorus are important elements found in healthy bones. Use a periodic table to find out whether calcium and phosphorus are metals or non-metals.

Apply

1 When babies are born the bones in their skulls are not fused together as they are in adults. This makes a baby's head soft and delicate. Give a reason why the bones in babies' skulls are not fused together.

2 The bones of birds are often hollow.

   a) Suggest a reason why this would be good for a bird.

   b) Suggest a reason why this might be bad for a bird.

» Joints

Worked example

Cartilage is a smooth tissue found at the end of bones. Explain the importance of cartilage. Try to give as much detail as you can.

Cartilage is really important because it protects the ends of the bones in a joint. Without cartilage the bones would rub together and wear away. This would cause a lot of pain and lead to arthritis. Cartilage is smooth so that it can reduce friction in the joint and allow the joint to move smoothly.

Hint

This question is encouraging you to go into detail. If you cannot remember what cartilage does, then look back through the pages of your Student Book to remind yourself.

Know

1 Copy and complete the following paragraph using your knowledge of joints. Use the words from the box.

cartilage	contract	friction	joint
ligaments	relax	tendons	

The adult human skeleton is made up of 206 bones, and where any two bones meet is called a _____. Pairs of muscles around a joint allow it to move because muscles are able to _____ (shorten) and _____ (lengthen). A joint has several different structures within it. For instance, _____ join muscle to bone, _____ connect one bone to another across a joint and _____ is a smooth tissue found at the end of bones, which reduces _____ between them.

Apply

1 Bicycle chains have lots of joints in them where the pieces of metal that make up the chain rub together. We lubricate bicycle chains to ensure that the chain runs smoothly. What does the same job as chain lubricant in a moving joint of a human skeleton?

2 When you curl your index finger, two joints in your finger move. Based on how your finger moves, what type of joint (pivot, hinge, or ball and socket) do you think is in your fingers? Justify your answer.

Hint

Justify means to give an explanation for something. So you need to explain why you chose your joint type.

3 Explain, using your knowledge of how your shoulder moves, why the joint in a shoulder is a ball-and-socket joint rather than a hinge joint.

4 There are 22 bones in an adult human skull and many joints. Almost none of these joints can move – they are fixed joints.

a) Which part of your skull can actually move?

b) Suggest what would happen to the shape of the skull if it contained moving joints.

c) Based on your answer to part b, suggest a reason for why the skull contains so many fixed joints.

Hint

This question gives a clear instruction about how you need to answer it. Your answer must include some information about how a shoulder can move.

» Antagonistic muscle pairs

Worked example

Describe, in detail, what happens to your quadriceps and hamstring (an antagonistic muscle pair) when you straighten your leg in front of you whilst sitting down.

When you are sitting down your leg is bent. The quadriceps muscles are relaxed and long but the hamstring is contracted and short. To straighten your leg the quadriceps must contract and shorten whilst the hamstring relaxes and lengthens.

Hint

This answer contains key terms used in your Student Book, like 'contract' and 'relaxes'. Try to use words like these in your answers too (when appropriate!).

Know

1 Copy and complete the following paragraph using your knowledge of antagonistic muscle pairs. Use the words from the box.

antagonistic	biceps	bones	hamstring	leg
movement	muscle	relax	shortening	triceps

Joints give flexibility and movement to a skeleton. Joints are where _____ meet and many joints in the human body can move because of the action of _____ _____ pairs. These are pairs of muscles working in unison to create _____. When one of the muscles in the pair is contracting (_____), the other muscle must _____ (lengthen), and these changes cause the joint to move. For example, to move your lower arm up, your _____ contracts, and your _____ muscle relaxes. To move your lower arm down the opposite occurs. An example of an antagonistic muscle pair in the _____ is the quadriceps and _____ muscle.

Apply

1 The muscles at the back of your lower leg are called calf muscles. The muscles at the front of your lower leg are your shin muscles. The calf and shin muscles are an antagonistic muscle pair that control the movement of your foot.

a) When you lift your foot so that your toes are pointing upward, which muscles are contracting and which are relaxing? Explain your answer.

b) Describe what happens to the calf and shin muscles when you go on your tiptoes.

2 Muscles are not just for moving bones at joints. The heart is a muscular organ in invertebrates that has a very important role. Why must the heart be made from muscle?

Hint

Try to explain your answer using ideas about lengthening and shortening of the two muscles.

Hint

If you are not sure, find out what the heart does on the internet and see if this helps.

16 Cells

» Comparing cells

Worked example

The cell membrane is a very important cell structure. Describe the function of the cell membrane, using keywords where appropriate.

The cell membrane surrounds the cell and keeps the contents of the cell in one place. It also allows substances to diffuse into and out of the cell, without which the cell would die.

Hint

'Diffuse' is a keyword that you hopefully understand and would think to use when writing about the cell membrane.

Know

1 Cells contain parts that can carry out the seven life process. What are the seven life processes?

2 Give the name of the part of a cell that contains genetic material, or DNA.

3 Animal cells and plant cells both contain cytoplasm. What is cytoplasm and why is it important?

4 Copy and complete the following paragraph, using your knowledge of the differences between plant and animal cells:

Many plant cells contain _____ which absorb light energy so that the plant can make food, but animal cells do not. In plant cells the cell membrane is surrounded by a _____ _____, but this is not present in animal cells. Inside a plant cell, but not in an animal cell, is an area that contains liquid, and can be used by plants to keep the cell rigid and store substances. It is called the _____.

Apply

1 Suggest two substances that might diffuse either into or out of a cell through the cell membrane.

2 In plants, chloroplasts are mostly concentrated in the cells of leaves. Suggest a reason for this.

3 The diagram shows a light microscope.

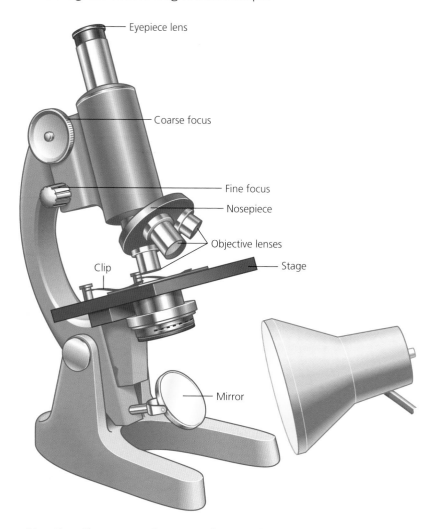

Eyepiece lens

Coarse focus

Fine focus

Nosepiece

Objective lenses

Clip

Stage

Mirror

Use the diagram and your understanding of how we observe cells to copy and complete the paragraph below, using the words in the box.

cover	eye	focus	image	microscopes
slip	small	stage	stain	

Cells are very _____, but we can use _____ to study them. When we prepare a microscope slide we often _____ the cells we want to observe. This helps us to see the internal structures of the cells (like vacuoles and nuclei) more clearly. We then cover our sample with a _____ _____ before placing the slide on the microscope _____ and looking at it through the _____ piece. We have to _____ the microscope carefully to ensure that we get a clear _____ of the cells we want to observe.

» Specialised animal cells

Worked example

As the diagram shows, the female egg cell (or ovum) in humans is very large in comparison with the sperm cell. It can be seen without the aid of a microscope.

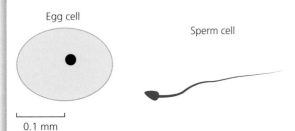

Egg cell

Sperm cell

0.1 mm

Suggest reasons for this structural adaptation.

The egg cell is large because it contains lots of cytoplasm that stores energy sources for the growing embryo. A large egg cell is also easier for the smaller sperm cells to find and fertilise.

Know

1 Many animal cells are specialised and have structural adaptations. What are structural adaptations?

2 You will have studied several specialised animal cells.

   a) Which cells have a branching structure to allow them to communicate with similar cells?

   b) Which cells have no nucleus, to maximise how much oxygen they can transport?

   c) Which cells contain a lot of mitochondria to release lots of energy through respiration?

Apply

1 The cell membrane of a red blood cell is very thin, allowing oxygen to dissolve in and out very quickly. Explain why this is beneficial for red blood cells.

2 Some human sperm cells have deformities, including shorter tail sections or a smaller tail base.

   a) Suggest and explain how a shorter tail might affect the sperm's ability to fertilise an egg cell.

   b) Suggest and explain how a smaller tail base might affect the sperm's ability to fertilise an egg cell.

3 Ciliated cells in the human body have tiny finger-like structures (called cilia) that are used to remove dust from the lungs and to waft the egg cell through the female reproductive system. Some unicellular organisms (made up of only one cell) also have rows of cilia on the surface of their cell. Suggest a reason for this structural adaptation in unicellular organisms.

≫ Specialised plant cells

Worked example

Explain why palisade cells are found in leaves, but not in the roots of a plant.

Palisade cells are specialised for photosynthesis – they have lots of chloroplasts, which are necessary for photosynthesis to take place. Leaves are exposed to sunlight, and this is also necessary for photosynthesis, so it makes sense that palisade cells are found in leaves. Roots are underground, and not exposed to sunlight, so photosynthesis cannot take place in roots. So there is no need for palisade cells in roots.

Know

1 Copy and complete the following paragraph, using your knowledge of specialised plant cells:

Two plant cells that are specialised for a particular function are root hair cells and phloem cells. Root hair cells have a large _____ _____ that helps them to absorb water and nutrients from the _____. Phloem cells have holes in their ends to allow _____ solution to travel through them. Plants use phloem cells to transport the sugars made during _____ in the leaves to where they are needed elsewhere in the plant for growth or storage.

Apply

1 The diagram on the right shows a group of xylem cells.

Xylem cells are used to transport water through the plant. They have structural adaptations to help them do this job.

a) What are structural adaptations?

b) Give two structural adaptations of xylem cells.

c) Explain how each of these two structural adaptations helps xylem cells to do their job.

2 Some plant cells (called sclerenchyma cells) have the job of supporting the plant as it grows. These cells help to keep the plant upright. They have a second cell wall that is strengthened by lignin.

a) From the information above, give the structural adaptation of sclerenchyma cells.

b) Suggest where in a plant you might find sclerenchyma cells: leaves, roots, flowers or stems?

c) What other plant cell has a similar adaptation to sclerenchyma cells?

3 It is not just palisade cells that contain chloroplasts. Chlorenchyma cells also contain chloroplasts.

a) What function can chlorenchyma cells carry out?

b) Other than in leaves, where else might you expect to find chlorenchyma cells? Explain your answer.

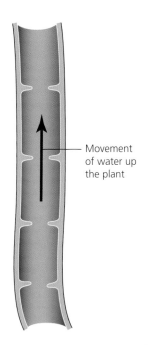

Movement of water up the plant

Hint

Don't panic! You don't need to know or pronounce the name of these cells.

» Organising cells

Worked example

An unknown specialised animal cell groups together to form tissue that is able to contract and relax by shortening and lengthening itself. Suggest what type of cell this animal cell might be, and in what organ system it is most likely to be found.

It must be a muscle cell as muscle cells would form muscle tissue, and muscles are able to contract (shorten) and relax (lengthen). The organ system is most likely to be the muscular–skeletal system, which supports, moves and protects an organism.

Know

1 Define the following terms:

   a) unicellular organism   b) multicellular organism.

2 Copy and complete the following paragraph, using your knowledge of how cells are organised:

   In multicellular organisms similar, specialised _____ are organised into _____, and these are organised into _____. For instance, muscle cells form muscle tissue, and muscle tissue makes up a lot of the heart in mammals. Different organs work together in organ _____ that carry out vital life _____. For instance, the heart and blood vessels make up the _____ system, which is responsible for transporting substances around the body.

3 Which human organ system is responsible for:

   a) protecting the body against infections

   b) producing sperm and eggs, and supporting a growing fetus

   c) supporting, moving and protecting the body

   d) replacing oxygen and removing carbon dioxide from the blood?

Apply

1 Multicellular organisms have organ systems to carry out the seven life processes; unicellular organisms, like bacteria, manage with just one cell.

   a) What structure of a bacterium helps it to move?

   b) What structure of a bacterium helps it to reproduce?

2 Copy and complete the following paragraph about the need for organ systems in multicellular organisms:

   Multicellular organisms need organ systems in order to carry out the seven _____ _____. In humans, _____ is achieved by the muscular–skeletal and nervous systems; _____ is achieved by the reproductive system; _____ is carried out by the respiratory and circulatory systems; and _____ and _____ are carried out by the digestive system.

17 Interdependence

» Classification

Worked example

What key feature of plants means that we classify them into a different group from animals?

The key feature of plants that makes them different from animals is that plants make their own food by a process called photosynthesis, whilst animals have to eat other organisms. During photosynthesis plants use the Sun's energy to convert carbon dioxide and water into sugars (their food) and oxygen gas.

Know

1 Copy and complete the following paragraph, using your knowledge of how we classify living things. Use the words in the box (some can be used more than once).

animals	bacteria	fungi	invertebrates
kingdoms	organisms	plants	vertebrates

Classification is a way in which we can group and name different living things, or _____ . Carl Linnaeus was an early pioneer of classification, and he came up with five big groups, or _____ . These were _____ , _____ , _____ , _____ and other single-celled organisms. Each of these groups is sub-divided further. For instance, the animal kingdom can be divided into two more groups: animals with a backbone (called _____) and animals without a backbone (called _____). For example, snails, worms, insects and crabs are all _____ , whilst mammals, birds, reptiles, amphibians and fish are all _____ .

Apply

1 We can classify organisms by the features or characteristics that they share. For instance, all birds have wings, whilst all reptiles are cold blooded and have dry, scaly skin.

   a) Which group of animals are warm-blooded, have hair or fur and feed their young on milk?

   b) Which group of animals are cold-blooded, breathe through gills and have scaly skin?

   c) Which group of animals are warm-blooded, lay eggs and are feathered?

   d) Which group of animals are cold-blooded, lay eggs in water and have moist skin?

2 At first glance, orcas (or killer whales) and sharks are very similar, but orcas are mammals and sharks are fish. Using this information, answer the following questions:

   a) Why do orcas have to come to the ocean surface regularly, whilst sharks don't?

   b) Sharks do not feed their young once they are born. What do orcas do?

   c) Orcas do actually have hair, but it is lost shortly after birth. Suggest why.

» Feeding relationships

Worked example

Describe the effect on a food chain of removing all the decomposers from an ecosystem, giving as much detail as you can.

Decomposers break down dead plant and animal matter, so that the nutrients they contain can be recycled by plants. Without decomposers plants would have less of the nutrients they need to grow. This would reduce the size of the producer trophic level, and then reduce the size of all the other trophic levels until the food chain collapsed.

Know

1 Copy and complete the following paragraph, using your knowledge of ecosystems, food chains and food webs. Use the words in the box.

ecosystem	photosynthesis	secondary	predator
producer	trophic	consumer	web

An _____ is made up of the living things in a given area and their non-living environment, within which there are food chains and food webs. A food chain starts with a _____ – a green plant or alga that makes its own food by _____. Any animal that eats this plant or alga is called a primary _____. Other animals can eat these primary consumers and are called _____ consumers, and so on. The top of a food chain is occupied by the top _____ – the animal that no other animal consumes. Each stage of a food chain is called a _____ level, and food chains can link up to form a food _____.

2 Give the term for:

   a) an organism that breaks down dead plant and animal material, so nutrients can be recycled back to the soil or water

   b) an animal that eats other animals or plants

   c) an animal that eats meat *and* plants or algae

   d) a group of the same species living in an area.

Apply

1 We grow food, eat food and often compost our food waste so that the nutrients it contains can be used to grow other plants. Are humans producers, consumers or decomposers? Explain your answer.

2 How high up a food chain or web would you expect humans to be? Explain your answer.

3 What would happen to the number of trophic levels in a food chain if more energy was transferred between trophic levels? Explain your answer.

» Pyramids of number and biomass

Worked example

What are the similarities and differences between a food chain and a pyramid of numbers?

Food chains and pyramids show which organisms consume others in an ecosystem, and they also show which way energy flows through the ecosystem. But a pyramid of number gives information about the numbers of living things in each population at each trophic level.

Know

1 Copy and complete the following paragraph, using your knowledge of pyramids of number. Use the words in the box.

chain	decreases	energy	first	fleas
imperfect	organisms	perfect	plant	wider

Pyramids of number show the number of _____ in each trophic level of a food _____ . Each trophic level is drawn as a horizontal bar and the _____ the bar, the greater the number of organisms. Usually, as we move up through the food chain, the number of organisms _____ quickly because only about 10% of the _____ of each trophic level is transferred to the next one, and fewer organisms can survive. So we get a _____ triangle shape. Sometimes we get an _____ triangle shape – this happens when one very large _____ , like a tree, forms the _____ trophic level. It can also happen when many parasitic organisms like _____ feed off the top predator in a food chain, causing a very wide top bar.

Apply

1 Two students are arguing about which type of pyramid is best: pyramids of number or pyramids of biomass.

a) What is biomass?

b) Give an advantage of pyramids of biomass over pyramids of number.

c) Give a disadvantage of pyramids of biomass.

2 Pyramids of energy can also be drawn in a similar way to pyramids of number and biomass. Each level of the pyramid shows the flow of energy from one level to the next. Will pyramids of energy be perfect or imperfect triangles? Explain your answer.

» Changes in ecosystems

Worked example

What is interdependence, and why does it happen?

Interdependence relates to the fact that all organisms in an ecosystem depend on each other, even if they are not in the same food chain. It happens because food chains are linked together into food webs, so a change to one organism in one trophic level can affect many other organisms across the food web.

Know

1 Copy and complete the following paragraph, using your knowledge of predator–prey cycles. Use the words in the box.

fall	more	predators	prey	rise
smaller	transferred	trophic		

_____ are animals that hunt and eat other animals, and _____ are the animals that are hunted. An example of a predator–prey relationship in the UK is barn owls and voles. In any ecosystem there are usually _____ prey than predators. This links to what we know about pyramids of number and biomass – each new _____ level gets _____ as we go up the pyramid because only about 10% of the energy in each level is _____ to the next. If a change in the ecosystem reduces the number of prey, then the number of predators will _____ because they have less food. If the change causes the number of predators to fall, then the number of prey will _____ as fewer of them are being hunted and killed.

Apply

1 A simple marine predator–prey pair is seals and sardines. The sardines feed on plankton (small organisms that float in the ocean). Seals are hunted by polar bears.

   a) Describe and explain the effect of the loss of plankton on the seal population in this ecosystem.

   b) Describe and explain the effect of a fall in polar bear numbers on the sardine population.

   c) In another food chain in the same ecosystem, orcas (killer whales) hunt and eat sardines. Describe and explain the effect of a rise in polar bear numbers on the orca population.

   d) What do these three questions give an example of?

18 Plant reproduction

» The life cycle of a plant

Worked example

Why is it important for plants to disperse their seeds, rather than have their offspring growing nearby?

Seed dispersal helps new plants to grow away from their parent plant, which increases the chance that the new plant will have enough nutrients and water from the soil it is growing in, and sunlight for photosynthesis. If a new plant grew close to its parent plant it would have to compete with its parent for nutrients, water and sunlight.

Know

1 The life cycle of a plant starts with a seed.

   a) Describe what happens during the germination of a seed.

   b) How do plants make their own food?

   c) What role can insects play in the life cycle of a flowering plant?

   d) What occurs during fertilisation in flowering plants?

   e) Give two examples of how a plant disperses (spreads) its seeds.

2 There are two types of plant: flowering and non-flowering.

   a) Give an example of a non-flowering plant.

   b) Give an example of a flowering plant that:

      i)   has brightly coloured flowers

      ii) has small, non-coloured flowers.

Apply

1 If a plant has brightly coloured flowers, what does this tell us about how it transfers its pollen to other plants?

2 A plant has small, uncolourful flowers. Suggest one method for how this plant transfers its pollen to other plants.

» Sexual reproduction

Worked example

Explain why plants benefit from reproducing sexually (i.e. with other plants of the same species).

By reproducing sexually, the new plants are likely to show greater variation, and this causes the gene pool of the plant species to widen. This is good because it means that the plants are more likely to be able to survive a change to their ecosystem that might otherwise have made them extinct.

Know

1 The diagram shows the structure of a flower.

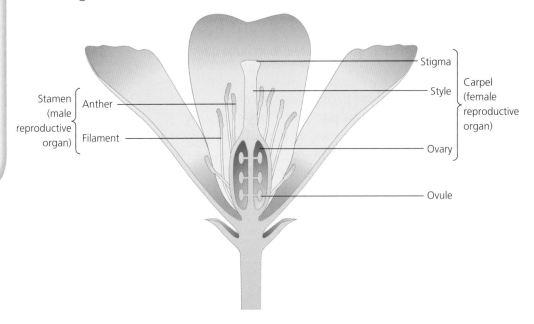

Give the terms for:

a) the joining of a nucleus from a male and female sex cell

b) the structure from where pollen grains are released

c) the structure that the ovary becomes after fertilisation, which contains seeds

d) the structure where pollen grains land during pollination

e) the structure that contains the embryo of a new plant.

Apply

1 The table below shows the stages that take place during the process of sexual reproduction of a plant. The stages are not in the correct order. Give each statement a number, indicating its order in the process.

Reproduction stage	Order
The fertilised egg develops into an embryo.	
The pollen grain forms a pollen tube, which grows down through the style towards the ovary.	
The ovule grows into the seed.	
A pollen grain from a different plant lands on the stigma of a flower.	
The ovary forms the fruit that surrounds the seed.	
The nucleus of the pollen grain containing DNA passes down the tube to fertilise the egg inside the ovule.	

2 Many of the plant structures involved in reproduction are adapted for their function.

   a) What is the function of fruit?

   b) Give an example of how fruits are adapted for their function.

   c) Give an example of how flowers of grasses are adapted for their function.

» Asexual reproduction

Worked example

What is the 'gene pool' of a population of organisms, and why is it important?

A gene pool is a measure of how much variation there is between organisms of the same species. If the gene pool is wide, it means that there is lots of variation between individual organisms, but if it is narrow there is little variation. The width of the gene pool is important because the wider it is, the better the chances are that the organisms can survive a harmful change to their ecosystem (like the introduction of a new predator).

Know

1 Give an example of a plant that uses runners to complete asexual reproduction.

2 During asexual reproduction, plants produce clones. What is a clone?

Apply

1 Describe the differences between asexual and sexual reproduction.

2 The table below shows the stages that take place during the process of asexual reproduction of a plant that uses runners. The stages are not in the correct order. Give each statement a number, indicating its order in the process.

Reproduction stage	Order
Small plantlets (or clones of the parent plant) develop on offshoots of the runner.	
The plantlets develop roots that grow into the soil and the clone plant continues to grow.	
A thin, flexible stem-like structure called a runner starts to grow at the base of the plant's stem.	
In this way, the clone plants do not share the same nutrients, sunlight and water that the parent plant needs.	
The runner grows horizontally along the ground.	

3 Describe an advantage of using runners during asexual reproduction instead of plantlets that fall from the parent plant's leaves.

4 Which plants are more likely to survive a harmful change in their ecosystem: plants that sexually reproduce, or those that asexually reproduce? Explain your answer.

» Seed dispersal

Worked example

Plants can disperse their seeds using wind, water and animals. What other method can they use to spread their seeds?

Some plants disperse their seeds by ejecting them forcibly from their pods. This shoots the seeds away from the plant.

Know

1 Copy and complete the following paragraph, using your knowledge of plant reproduction and seed dispersal. Use the words in the box.

animals	blown	egestion	float	fruit
lightweight	nucleus	ovule	pollen	stigma	wind

During sexual reproduction in plants, a plant is pollinated and fertilised – _____ from one plant is transferred to the _____ of another, and the _____ from the pollen grain fertilises the egg. The _____ then develops into the seed, and how this seed is dispersed varies between plants. Some plants, like dandelions, make seeds that are _____ and can be easily _____ away from the parent by the _____. Other plants make seeds that can _____, and so can disperse from the parent plant on water. Other plants rely on _____ to carry their seeds away. One way they do this is by making _____ that encourages animals to eat them and expel the seeds somewhere else by _____.

Apply

1 Swan plants, like dandelions, produce seeds that are easily carried large distances by the wind. What is the benefit of producing seeds like this?

2 When we eat a tomato or a strawberry, we eat the seeds as well as the fruit that surrounds them. Why don't the seeds get broken down by our digestive systems?

3 Which method of seed dispersal – wind, water or animal – is most likely to get the seed furthest from the plant? Explain your answer.

19 Variation

» Examples of variation

Worked example

An example of variation between different species of bear is their fur colour. How does this help them to adapt to their environment?

The white fur of polar bears makes it easier for them to hunt their prey. Their fur colour camouflages well with the snow and ice that they hunt on, and allows them to approach prey without being spotted. Brown and black bears would be easily seen in the icy environments that polar bears live and hunt in.

Know

1 Dogs are a popular pet across the UK, and are also used as working animals on farms, at airports and for the police.

    a) What animal do all dogs originate from?

    b) There is a huge variety of dogs now due to selective breeding. What type of selection is selective breeding an example of: natural or artificial?

    c) What characteristics make golden retrievers a good choice for a family pet?

    d) Give two characteristics that would be good for a dog used to detect drugs in airport luggage.

2 Selective breeding can reduce the variation in certain breeds of animals like dogs. Why is this a problem?

Apply

1 Jack Russell terriers were originally bred about 200 years ago to hunt foxes. They have small, muscular bodies and are intelligent and vocal (they bark a lot). Explain why these characteristics were chosen for this breed of dog.

» Causes of variation

Worked example

Dan and Greg are unrelated and Dan is taller than Greg. Explain why this variation in their heights could be an example of genetic and environmental variation.

Dan could have inherited genes that make him naturally taller than Greg, meaning that the height difference was an example of genetic variation. But he could also have had a better diet than Greg as he was growing up, so he grew taller. This would make it an example of environmental variation.

Know

1 Copy and complete the following paragraph, using your knowledge about species and breeding. Use the words in the box.

breed	donkey	fertile	infertile
horse	species	species	

A _____ is a group of living things that have more in common with each other than with other groups. Different organisms of one species are able to interbreed and have _____ offspring. For instance, a golden retriever can breed with a cocker spaniel, and the puppies would be able to _____ as well. Organisms from different species may be able to breed, but their offspring will be _____ . This means that the offspring cannot breed themselves. For example, a mule can never produce an offspring because it was made when a _____ and _____ bred, and these animals are not in the same _____ .

2 Variation can mean the differences between individual organisms within a species (intraspecific variation), and also the difference between different species (interspecific variation).

   a) Give an example of variation in dogs.

   b) Give an example of variation between lions and cheetahs.

3 What are the two causes of variation?

Apply

1 For the following examples of variation within a species, state whether the variation is an example of genetic or environmental variation, or both:

   a) two giraffes with different heights

   b) one dog with brown eyes and another with pale blue eyes

   c) one person with short hair and another with long hair

   d) one person with naturally red hair, and another with naturally blonde hair.

2 Imagine that two genetically identical twins grow up separately, and by the time they are adults, one has darker skin than the other. Explain how this could happen.

» Types of data

Worked example

There is a relationship between the height of a human and their arm span. The greater the height, the longer the arm span. What type of variation is height and arm span, and how might it be caused?

Height and arm span are both examples of continuous variation because they both come in a range of values. Height and arm span could be caused by genetic variation or environmental variation.

> **Hint**
>
> There are two parts to this question, so the answer should answer them both.

Know

1 For each of the following examples of variation, state whether it is continuous or discontinuous variation:

   a) weight

   b) shoulder width

   c) flower colour

   d) hair colour

   e) leg length.

Apply

1 A student decided to survey her classmates' height. She measured each classmate's height and recorded the following data:

Height of classmate in cm	Number of classmates with this height
140	1
145	2
148	3
150	4
154	5
157	4
161	3
165	2
168	1

   a) What sort of variable is the height of her classmates: continuous or discontinuous?

   b) What sort of graph should the student draw to represent her data?

   c) Plot a line graph with 'height of classmate' on the *x*-axis and 'number of classmates with this height' on the *y*-axis. Draw a smooth line through your data points. The type of pattern shown here is called a 'bell curve'. Suggest why.

2   In the UK blood donors donate blood to help other people who need blood. It is important that a patient gets the right blood type. There are eight different blood groups, as shown in the table below:

Blood type	Percentage of donations of that blood type (%)
O+	36
A+	30
B+	8
AB+	2
O–	13
A–	8
B–	2
AB–	1

a) What type of variation is blood type: environmental or genetic? Give a reason for your answer.

b) What type of variable is blood type: continuous or discontinuous? Give a reason for your answer.

c) What sort of graph should we use to represent these data?

d) Draw a graph of these data with 'blood type' on the x-axis and 'percentage of donations of that blood type' on the y-axis.

» Why is variation important?

Worked example

Selective breeding of pug dogs has resulted in pugs having a very narrow gene pool. Explain how this would affect the breed's ability to survive a change to their environment.

Because there is so little variation in the breed, each pug dog has the same ability to adapt to a change in their environment. So any change that occurs that any one pug cannot adapt to, will affect all the other pugs in the same way.

Know

1   Copy and complete the paragraph at the top of the next page, using your knowledge of biodiversity and its benefits. Use the words in the box.

biodiversity	variation	environment	extinct
gene	inbred	pool	species

Variation is a measure of the differences within and between
_____ . A similar measure is _____ , which is the variety of
living things. We know that species that show a lot of _____ are
more able to cope with change to their _____ , and this is because
with greater variation there is a wider _____ _____ . Species
that can adapt to changes in their environment are less likely to become
_____ than those that cannot. Animals, like dogs, that have been
bred to have certain characteristics can often have a very narrow gene
pool, and we say the animal is _____ .

Apply

1 Polar bears are highly adapted to their Arctic environment. They have
many characteristics that enable them to live in a very challenging
environment.

    a) Describe and explain two characteristics of polar bears that help them
to live in the Arctic.

    b) The Arctic environment is changing rapidly due to global warming, and
there is concern that polar bears may become extinct. What will help
polar bears to survive this change?

2 Explain how variation in a population of giant tortoises on a remote island
would help the population to survive a disease that was brought to the
island when a new tortoise was left there.

> **Hint**
>
> If you cannot
> think of any, go
> online and search
> for 'polar bear
> adaptations'.

20 Human reproduction

GENES

» The life cycle of a human

Worked example

Ethical questions, such as 'when is a developing embryo a "life"?' are difficult to answer, and cannot be approached using science alone. Explain why.

The answer depends upon the opinions of people, and people will have many different opinions based on their religious beliefs, their morals (what they think is right or wrong) and other factors. Science cannot answer these questions because they are a matter of opinion rather than something that can be answered by carrying out an experiment.

Know

1 Copy and complete the following paragraph, using your knowledge about the human life cycle. Use the words in the box.

Once fertilisation occurs a human is just one _____, and this cell quickly divides and copies itself many times. After 5 weeks of this, we call the developing human an _____, and then from 11 weeks we call it a _____. After _____ months, a baby is born and _____ begins. _____ starts when the child becomes a teenager, and during this stage of the human life cycle, _____ takes place. Puberty is a series of _____ to teenagers' bodies that result in them being able to sexually reproduce. _____ follows adolescence, and is the longest stage of the cycle. The human life cycle ends with _____ _____. This stage is getting longer and longer as healthcare improves and people live for longer.

| adolescence |
| adulthood |
| age |
| cell |
| changes |
| childhood |
| embryo |
| fetus |
| 9 |
| old |
| puberty |

2 Puberty is an important stage in the human life cycle that involves many changes to both boys' and girls' bodies.

a) Give three examples of changes that take place in boys during puberty.

b) Give three examples of changes that take place in girls during puberty.

c) Over what age range does puberty start in teenagers, and how long does it usually last?

Apply

1 During the very early stages of pregnancy, the fertilised egg is called a zygote – a single cell that slowly begins to divide to form new cells. After 5 weeks the growing human is called an embryo, and after 8–11 weeks it is called a foetus.

a) During cell division, one cell divides to form two new cells. These two new cells can carry out cell division as well, forming four new cells.

With each cell division, the number of cells doubles. Assuming that this cell division takes 24 hours, how many cells will be present in the developing zygote after 10 days?

b) As the zygote divides, it slowly moves along the inside of the mother's reproductive organs. It covers a distance of about 10 cm in around 1 week. Calculate the approximate speed of a zygote in centimetres per hour (cm/hr).

» The male and female reproductive systems

Worked example

The diagram on the right shows a sperm cell.

This is an example of a cell with structural adaptations that make it very good at its job. Describe and explain the structural adaptations of a sperm cell.

Sperm cells have a tail that they use to swim towards the egg. They have lots of mitochondria at the base of their tails, which release lots of energy that they use to swim to the egg.

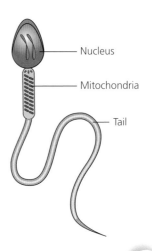

Nucleus

Mitochondria

Tail

Know

1 The reproductive system is responsible for sexual reproduction in humans. It is an example of an organ system.

   a) What is an organ system?

   b) Give three examples of other organ systems in humans.

2 The diagram shows the female reproductive system.

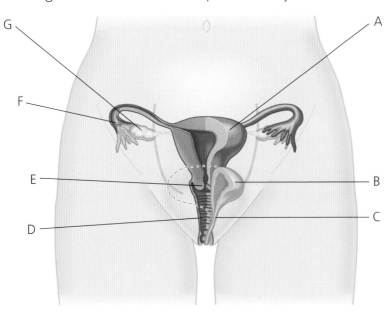

Hint

You may need to look back to Chapter 16 if you cannot remember the definition of an organ system.

Using the diagram, give the label (A–G) and the name of each of the following structures within the female reproductive system:

a) the organ that contains eggs

b) where the penis enters the female's body and sperm is received

c) where a baby develops in a pregnant woman

d) the structure that carries an egg from the ovary to the uterus and where fertilisation occurs

e) the opening through which sperm cells pass into the uterus.

3 The diagram shows the male reproductive system.

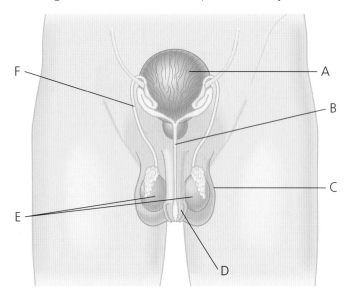

Using the diagram, give the label (A–F) and the name of each of the following structures within the male reproductive system:

a) the organs where sperm cells are produced

b) the organ that carries sperm cells out of the male's body.

Apply

1 The following table contains seven statements that describe the process of sexual reproduction and fertilisation in humans. The statements are not in the correct order. Give each statement a number (1–7) showing the correct order.

Statement	Order
During ejaculation the semen enters the woman's vagina near the cervix.	
Many sperm then enter the fallopian tubes (or oviducts).	
Many millions of sperm are released from testicles and mix with a nutrient-rich fluid, forming semen.	
The fertilised egg is wafted into the uterus by ciliated cells that line the fallopian tubes.	
Millions of sperm swim through the cervix and enter the uterus (or womb).	
The fertilised egg then settles into the lining of the uterus and develops into a baby.	
One sperm finds and enters the egg and fertilises it.	

» The menstrual cycle

Worked example

What are hormones, how do they work and why are they important?

Hormones are molecules produced by the body that control lots of important processes like puberty, the menstrual cycle and your blood sugar. They work by being released into the bloodstream from glands in the body. They eventually enter their target organ and cause a change in that organ or how it works.

Know

1 Copy and complete the following paragraph, using your knowledge about the menstrual cycle. Use the words in the box.

embryo
fertilised
menstruation
period
pregnancy
ovaries
ovulation
settles
sperm
start
stops
thicken

The menstrual cycle prepares the female for _____ and stops if the egg is fertilised by a _____. On average, it is a 28-day cycle that starts on day 1 with the loss of the lining of the uterus. We call this _____ and it is often called having a _____. After menstruation has occurred, the lining of the uterus begins to _____ again in preparation for a _____ egg. On day 14 _____ happens – an egg cell is released from one of the _____ and this egg may be met by a sperm and fertilised. If fertilisation does not occur, then the uterus lining remains thick until the last day of the cycle, and is then lost during menstruation at the _____ of the next cycle. If fertilisation does occur, then the fertilised egg _____ into the uterus lining and develops into an _____. The lining is not lost, and the menstrual cycle _____.

Apply

1 Describe what is happening within the female reproductive system at the following times during a typical menstrual cycle of a woman. Use as many key words in your answers as you can.

a) day 14

b) days 1 to 4

c) days 15–28 (if the egg is *not* fertilised)

d) days 15–28 (if the egg *is* fertilised)

2 Hormones are important biological molecules that control many processes in the human body. Oestrogen and progesterone are two important hormones for the menstrual cycle.

a) Describe how the levels of oestrogen in a woman's bloodstream affect the menstrual cycle.

b) Describe how the levels of progesterone in a woman's bloodstream affect the menstrual cycle.

» Gestation and birth

Worked example

Describe how some mammals, like koalas and kangaroos, have a different gestation from other mammals, like cats, humans and giraffes.

Koalas and kangaroos have short gestation periods, and at the end of gestation the baby koala or kangaroo climbs into its mother's pouch, where the rest of its development takes place. Koalas and kangaroos are examples of marsupials.

Hint

Marsupials are a group of mammals that carry their young in a pouch.

Know

1 The diagram shows a stage of pregnancy.

   Using the diagram, give the label (A–G) and the name of each of the following structures:

   a) the developing baby during pregnancy

   b) the organ that provides the fetus with oxygen and nutrients and removes waste substances

   c) the structure that connects the fetus to the placenta

   d) the liquid that surrounds and protects the fetus.

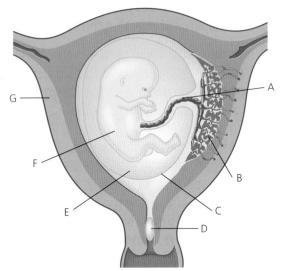

2 The placenta plays an essential role in the growth and development of a fetus.

   a) What *essential* substances diffuse through the placenta from the mother to the fetus?

   b) What substances diffuse through the placenta from the fetus to the mother?

Apply

1 Explain why pregnant women are advised not to smoke or drink a lot of alcohol during pregnancy.

2 The following table contains six statements that describe the process of birth in humans. The statements are not in the correct order. Copy the table and put a number beside each statement (1–6), showing the correct order.

Statement	Order
The muscles of the uterus undergo a series of involuntary contractions.	
The placenta passes from the uterus through the vagina.	
The baby moves from the uterus, through the narrow opening of the cervix, to the vagina.	
The amniotic sac surrounding the baby bursts and releases the amniotic fluid, which passes from the vagina.	
The baby's head is usually born first, followed by the rest of its body.	
The umbilical cord is cut and the baby takes its first breath.	

3 What are cravings, and what is a possible explanation for why some pregnant women have them?

GENES

Index

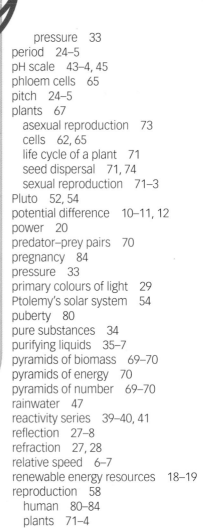